FORMULAS FOR THE NUMERICAL SOLUTION OF PARTIAL DIFFERENTIAL EQUATIONS BY THE METHOD OF DIFFERENCES

D. J. PANOV

FORMULAS FOR THE NUMERICAL SOLUTION OF PARTIAL DIFFERENTIAL EQUATIONS BY THE METHOD OF DIFFERENCES

Translated by Charles M. Stern

FREDERICK UNGAR PUBLISHING CO.
NEW YORK

Printed in the United States of America

Library of Congress Catalog Card No. 63-12911

FOREWORD

Many of the problems of modern technological theory are reducible to the solution of boundary value problems for partial differential equations. However, the practical solution of such problems presents considerable difficulties, and science has hitherto lacked a method of solution that completely satisfied the engineer's requirements. The analytical methods that have certainly been brilliantly perfected from the theoretical point of view have scarcely proved of practical use because of the extraordinary complexity of the computations to which they lead in such problems that have practical significance. Moreover, in many cases these methods may generally be left unused because the boundary of the domain, the boundary values of the required function, and much else besides are frequently not expressed by any suitable analytical formula. In all such cases the scientist must resort to the methods of *approximate* solution for boundary value problems to which an increasingly important place has been given of late in scientific as well as mathematical literature as far as practical applications are concerned.

The methods of approximate solution of boundary value problems for partial differential equations can be divided into two main groups:

a) Methods that produce an approximate *analytical* expression for the required function;

b) Numerical or graphical methods that produce numerical values for this, that, or the other variable but give no analytical expression for the function required.

The former group comprises the Ritz method extremely popular with engineers, the Galerkin method, and a whole series of methods cognate with the Ritz method but propounded by L. V. Kantorovich [R. 31]*, and a number of others.

First place in the second group is taken by the *method of differences*, which is the principal feature of the present volume, though a number of graphical methods (Runge, etc.) are also included.

The methods of the first group frequently turn out to be most practical, although the class of problems to which they are applicable is exceedingly restricted due to the need to employ analytical expressions for the equations for the boundary, boundary values, etc.

The methods of the second group are of more universal application. There is hardly any need to introduce restrictions into them on account of the conditions of the

---

*Square bracket references are to the bibliography starting on p. 129.

problems as they occur in practice, and this constitutes their chief value. It is to be regretted that these methods, whose development dates back only some forty years or so, are not yet better known to engineers. In the present volume we have endeavored to assemble the heterogeneous data on the practical application of these methods, and organize all this material along a definite line. As the field of applied mathematics under consideration here is still fairly new, and to many people quite novel, we have ventured to amplify the traditional form of mathematical formulary by explaining the formulas to some extent and adding a number of relevant numerical examples. This volume, therefore, represents something approximately halfway between a formulary strictly so-called and a practical textbook for the numerical solution of partial differential equations.

The solution of boundary value problems for the Laplace differential equation forms the principal part of this compendium. This kind of arrangement for the book is justified, to our mind, on the following grounds:

1. The solution of boundary value problems for the Laplace equation is one of the particularly important problems in applied mathematics.

2. The solution of such problems demands comparatively more work, for instance, than the solution of partial differential equations of the parabolic or hyperbolic types.

3. Essential features of the method of differences are especially well highlighted in the solution of boundary value problems for the Laplace equation.

This third edition includes a number of additions to the first two, particularly in reference to the solution of hyperbolic equations after the method of characteristics.

D. J. P.

I. INTRODUCTION

1. *The Method of Differences for the Solution of Differential Equations*

The essence of the method of differences for the solution of differential equations is that instead of solving a differential equation one solves a corresponding finite difference equation that is obtained by substituting difference expressions with higher or lower level of accuracy for the derivatives. Thus, for instance, the Laplace differential equation

$$\frac{\partial^2 u}{\partial x^2} + \frac{\partial^2 u}{\partial y^2} = 0 \tag{1}$$

is replaced by the difference equation

$$u_{xx} + u_{yy} = 0, \tag{2}$$

in which u_{xx} and u_{yy} denote the partial second differences with respect to x and y:

$$\left. \begin{array}{l} u_{xx} = \dfrac{1}{h^2}\,[u\,(x+h,\,y) - 2u\,(x,\,y) + u\,(x-h,\,y)], \\[2mm] u_{yy} = \dfrac{1}{h^2}\,[u\,(x,\,y+h) - 2u\,(x,\,y) + u\,(x,\,y-h)]. \end{array} \right\} \tag{3}$$

If more accurate expressions than those given in formula (3) are used for the derivatives, the difference equation (2) becomes more complicated.

It is important to note, moreover, that on substitution of the differential equation, a difference equation is obtained that combines the values of the required function only in individual, discretely distributed points. The points are usually chosen so as to form a quadrate network.

The method of differences is especially suitable for the solution of boundary value problems, for instance, the problem of determining a function that satisfies the Laplace equation in the interior of a given field G and possesses given values at the boundary of the field; such problems arise in the exploration of stationary temperature distribution when the temperature at the boundary of the field is known, in investigating the tension in a twisted rod of prismatic section, etc. etc. In such cases, the procedure is as follows:

After a definite number h (length of interval or width of mesh) has been fixed, a network is constructed on the x,y plane (Fig. 1) covering the field G and consisting of two systems of mutually perpendicular straight lines having the interval h between them. In this network a boundary is described which approximates as closely as possible to the boundary of the given field. This boundary intercepts a new field $\bar{G}$ (*network field*). The limiting values given on the boundary Γ of the field G are transferred to the boundary $\bar{\Gamma}$ of field $\bar{G}$ by some suitable method. Following this operation, instead of the boundary value problem of the differential equation for field G, the corresponding boundary value problem of the difference equation for field $\bar{G}$ can be solved. As previously stated, the difference equation combines only the values of the required function at the points of the net; on the determination of which the whole problem is resolved.

If the difference expressions given in formula (3) are substituted in equation (2), we obtain the equation:

$$u(x+h,\,y) + u(x-h,\,y) + u(x,\,y+h) + u(x,\,y-h) - 4u(x,\,y) = 0. \qquad (4)$$

Such an equation must be satisfied for every point (x, y) in the interior of field $\bar{G}$. If there are N such points, then if such an equation has been written down for each of them, N equations are obtained with N unknowns (the values of function u at the

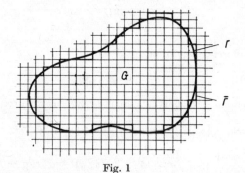

Fig. 1

points under consideration). If the original differential equation was linear, then this set will consist of linear equations. Some of these equations will be homogeneous (for such points, where there is no boundary point adjacent to them), some will be inhomogeneous (for points near the boundary of field $\bar{G}$, where the values of the function required are given beforehand). Accordingly the solution of a boundary value problem by the method of differences is reduced simply to the solution of a set of linear equations, of course with a tremendous number of unknowns (often several hundred). The solution of such a set will be possible only if it consists of extraordinarily simple equations, such as equation (4) for instance. In such case the solution can be effected by means of the method of iteration.

2. Solution of Difference Equations by the Method of Iteration

To solve the difference equation that replaces the original differential equation or, what is the same thing, to resolve the set of linear equations that is equivalent to the difference equation to be considered, the method of iteration is used. Suppose, for instance, that equation (2) or its equivalent equation (4) is to be solved on the assumption that the values of the function required on the boundary of field $\bar{G}$ are given. Equation (4) can be rearranged in the form

$$u(x, y) = \frac{u(x+h, y) + u(x-h, y) + u(x, y+h) + u(x, y-h)}{4}$$

and a function is sought such that it assumes the given values at the boundary of the field and is equal to the mean value of its four adjacent points at each internal point. We assume arbitrary values at all the internal points of field $\bar{G}$, and call this set of values set no. 1. At all internal points we form the mean of the adjacent values of set no. 1, and call the new set of values set no. 2 (the boundary values remain always invariably equal to the given values; they are equal to one another in both set no. 1 and set no. 2). From set no. 2, in exactly the same way, set no. 3 is obtained, and so on. The process of iteration comes to an end when, in the limits of accuracy prescribed, set no. $n + 1$ coincides with set no. n. Obviously set no. n then gives such values as satisfy equation (4) in the interior of field $\bar{G}$ and are, on the boundary of the field, equal to those given, i.e. this set represents the solution of the problem. It can be shown that the process described is, in fact, convergent [R40].

II. GENERAL PART

Table of Differences. For convenient transcription of successive values of the differences of a given function of one variable $f(x)$ an array (see Table 1) is used.

TABLE 1

Array for the Computation of Successive Differences

k	x	f	f'	f''	f'''	f^{IV}	f^{V}	f^{VI}
...	...	...						
-2	x_{-2}	f_{-2}		f''_{-2}		f^{IV}_{-2}		f^{VI}_{-2}
$-3/2$			$f'_{-3/2}$		$f'''_{-3/2}$		$f^{V}_{-3/2}$	
-1	x_{-1}	f_{-1}		f''_{-1}		f^{IV}_{-1}		f^{VI}_{-1}
$-1/2$			$f'_{-1/2}$		$f'''_{-1/2}$		$f^{V}_{-1/2}$	
0	x_0	f_0		f''_0		f^{IV}_0		f^{VI}_0
$+1/2$			$f'_{1/2}$		$f'''_{1/2}$		$f^{V}_{1/2}$	
$+1$	x_1	f_1		f''_1		f^{IV}_1		f^{VI}_1
$+3/2$			$f'_{3/2}$		$f'''_{3/2}$		$f^{V}_{3/2}$	
$+2$	x_2	f_2		f''_2		f^{IV}_2		f^{VI}_2
$+5/2$			$f'_{5/2}$		$f'''_{5/2}$		$f^{V}_{5/2}$	
...	...	...						

Each difference in this table is obtained by subtracting each number from the one succeeding it in a given column and suffixing it with the subscript equal to the mean of the subscripts of the numbers from which it is formed.

General formula for computation of the differences of a function of one variable:

$$f^{(\varkappa)}_m - f^{(\varkappa)}_{m-1} = f^{(\varkappa+1)}_{m-1/2}.$$

In the case of a function of *two* variables, it is not possible to build up a difference array on the plane. The notation is similar to that used for a function of a single variable, though, of course, two pairs of indices must be used; two superscripts and two subscripts. Each pair (the superscript and the corresponding subscript) relates to one of the variables ([G60], p. 108).

1. *Interpolation Formulae*

For the computation of intermediate values of a function in such cases where its values are known only for individual points, *interpolation formulae* are used. In the solution of differential equations by the method of differences, one is dealing directly with values of the function at individual points (at the grid intersections of the network); it is, therefore, natural that interpolation formulae prove to be an important aid in the solution of the problem by this method. Especially must interpolation

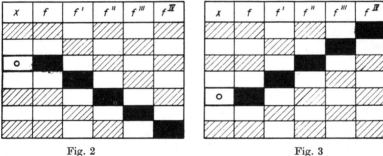

Fig. 2   Fig. 3

formulae be used on the transfer of boundary values from the actual boundary of the field to the approximate boundary of the net.

Below are shown a few calculations in connection with interpolation formulae as well as the necessary formula material.

Each formula is accompanied by an array of the differences entering into it (Figs. 2, 3, 4, and 5). The array looks like a net, in which the places for the differences are cross-hatched, the differences that enter into the composition of the formula being shown in solid black. The value x_0 is specially marked with a circle. We denote by h the constant interval between values of x, for which the values of $f(x)$ are given.

The variable t which appears in all the formulae dealt with below is connected with x by the relation
$$x = x_0 + th$$

or
$$t = \frac{x - x_0}{h}$$

It is obvious that the values $x = x_0, x_0 + h, x_0 + 2h, \ldots$ correspond to the values $t = 0, 1, 2, \ldots$

A. NEWTON's formula for Forward Interpolation (Fig. 2)

$$f(x_0 + th) = f_0 + t f'_{1/2} + \frac{t(t-1)}{2!} f''_1 + \frac{t(t-1)(t-2)}{3!} f'''_{3/2} + \cdots$$

$$\cdots + \frac{t(t-1)\,t-2)(\ldots(t-n+1)}{n!} f^{(n)}_{n/2} + R_n.$$

Remainder: $R_n = \binom{t}{n+1} h^{n+1} f^{n+1}(x_0 + \tau h) =$

$$= \frac{t(t-1)(t-2)\ldots(t-n)}{(n+1)!} h^{n+1} f^{(n+1)}(x_0 + \tau h); \quad (0 \leqq \tau \leqq n)[1].$$

It is postulated that the formula is used for **interpolation**, i.e. $0 \leqq t \leqq n$.

The **values of the coefficients** for this formula are set out in Table 2 (p. 7).

B. Newton's Formula for Backward Interpolation (Fig. 3)

$$f(x_0 + th) = f_0 + t f'_{-1/2} + \frac{t(t+1)}{2!} f''_{-1} + \frac{t(t+1)(t+2)}{3!} f'''_{-3/2} + \cdots$$

$$\cdots + \frac{t(t+1)(t+2)\ldots(t+n-1)}{n!} f^{(n)}_{-n/2} + R_n.$$

Remainder: $R_n = \binom{t+n}{n+1} h^{n+1} f^{(n+1)}(x_0 + \tau h) =$

$$= \frac{t(t+1)(t+2)\ldots(t+n)}{(n+1)!} h^{n+1} f^{(n+1)}(x_0 + \tau h); \quad (0 \leqq \tau \leqq n).$$

(Provided $0 \leqq t \leqq n$).

The **values of the coefficients** for this formula can be obtained from Table 2; if $-t$ is substituted for t in the expressions for the coefficients of the Newton forward interpolation formula, the coefficient for the Newton formula for backward interpolation is then obtained with its corresponding sign. This formula is therefore used especially frequently for negative values of t.

C. STIRLING's Formula (Fig. 4)

$$f(x_0 + th) = f_0 + t f'_0 + \frac{t^2}{2!} f''_0 + \frac{t(t^2-1)}{3!} f'''_0 + \frac{t^2(t^2-1)}{4!} f^{IV}_0 +$$

$$+ \frac{t(t^2-1)(t^2-4)}{5!} f^V_0 + \frac{t^2(t^2-1)(t^2-4)}{6!} f^{VI}_0 + \cdots$$

Here the odd differences are used with *integral* index; they must be considered as the **semi-sum** of adjacent differences of the same order:

---

[1]Here and at later points in this book, n denotes the order of the final difference that appears in the interpolation formula.

TABLE 2

Coefficients for the Newton Interpolation Formula

t	$\dfrac{t(t-1)}{2!}$	$\dfrac{t(t-1)(t-2)}{3!}$	$\dfrac{t(t-1)(t-2)(t-3)}{4!}$
0,00	—0,00000	+0,0000	—0,0000
01	00495	0033	0024
02	00980	0065	0048
03	01455	0096	0071
04	01920	0125	0093
0,05	—0,02375	+0,0154	—0,0114
06	02820	0182	0134
07	03255	0209	0153
08	03680	0236	0172
09	04095	0261	0190
0,10	—0,04500	+0,0285	—0,0207
11	04895	0308	0223
12	05280	0331	0238
13	05655	0352	0253
14	06020	0373	0267
0,15	—0,06375	+0,0393	—0,0280
16	06720	0412	0293
17	07055	0430	0304
18	07380	0448	0316
19	07695	0464	0326
0,20	—0,08000	+0,0480	—0,0336
21	08295	0495	0345
22	08580	0509	0354
23	08855	0522	0362
24	09120	0535	0369
0,25	—0,09375	+0,0547	—0,0376
26	09620	0558	0382
27	09855	0568	0388
28	10080	0578	0393
29	10295	0587	0398
0,30	—0,10500	+0,0595	—0,0402
31	10695	0602	0405
32	10880	0609	0408
33	11055	0615	0411
34	11220	0621	0413
0,35	—0,11375	+0,0626	—0,0415
36	11520	0630	0416
37	11655	0633	0416
38	11780	0636	0417
39	11895	0638	0416
0,40	—0,12000	+0,0640	—0,0416
41	12095	0641	0415
42	12180	0641	0414
43	12255	0641	0412
44	12320	0641	0410

Continuation of Table 2

t	$\dfrac{t(t-1)}{2!}$	$\dfrac{t(t-1)(t-2)}{3!}$	$\dfrac{t(t-1)(t-2)(t-3)}{4!}$
0,45	−0,12375	+0,0639	−0,0408
46	12420	0638	0405
47	12455	0635	0402
48	12480	0632	0398
49	12496	0629	0395
0,50	−0,12500	+0,0625	−0,0391
51	12495	0621	0386
52	12480	0616	0382
53	12455	0610	0377
54	12420	0604	0372
0,55	−0,12375	+0,0598	−0,0366
56	12320	0591	0361
57	12255	0584	0355
58	12180	0576	0349
59	12095	0568	0342
0,60	−0,12000	+0,0560	−0,0336
61	11895	0551	0392
62	11780	0542	0322
63	11655	0532	0315
64	11520	0522	0308
0,65	−0,11375	+0,0512	−0,0301
66	11220	0501	0293
67	11055	0490	0285
68	10880	0479	0278
69	10695	0467	0270
0,70	−0,10500	+0,0455	−0,0262
71	10295	0443	0253
72	10080	0430	0245
73	09855	0417	0237
74	09620	0404	0228
0,75	−0,09375	+0,0391	−0,0220
76	09120	0377	0211
77	08855	0363	0202
78	08580	0349	0194
79	08295	0335	0185
0,80	−0,08000	+0,0320	−0,0176
81	07695	0305	0167
82	07380	0290	0158
83	07055	0275	0149
84	06720	0260	0140
0,85	−0,06375	+0,0244	−0,0131
86	06020	0229	0122
87	05655	0213	0113
88	05280	0197	0104
89	04895	0181	0095

Continuation of Table 2

t	$\dfrac{t(t-1)}{2!}$	$\dfrac{t(t-1)(t-2)}{3!}$	$\dfrac{t(t-1)(t-2)(t-3)}{4!}$
0,90	−0,04500	+0,0165	−0,0087
91	04095	0149	0078
92	03680	0132	0069
93	03255	0116	0060
94	02820	0100	0051
0,95	−0,02375	+0,0083	−0,0043
96	01920	0067	0034
97	01455	0050	0025
98	00980	0033	0017
99	00495	0017	0008
1,00	−0,00000	+0,0000	−0,0000

$$f_0' = \frac{1}{2}[f_{1/2}' + f_{-1/2}']; \quad f_0''' = \frac{1}{2}[f_{1/2}''' + f_{-1/2}'''].$$

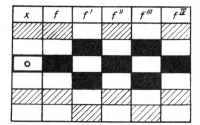

Fig. 4

Remainder:

a) n even:

$$R_n = \begin{pmatrix} t + \dfrac{n}{2} \\ n+1 \end{pmatrix} h^{n+1} f^{(n+1)}(x_0 + \tau h) =$$

$$= \frac{t(t^2-1)(t^2-4)\ldots\left(t^2 - \dfrac{n^2}{4}\right)}{(n+1)!} h^{n+1} f^{(n+1)}(x_0 + \tau h) \quad (0 \le \tau \le n).$$

b) n odd (It is of no advantage to use the Stirling formula in this case):

$$R_n = \frac{h^{n+1}}{2}\left[\begin{pmatrix} t + \dfrac{n-1}{2} \\ n+1 \end{pmatrix} f^{(n+1)}(x_0 + \tau_1 h) + \begin{pmatrix} t + \dfrac{n+1}{2} \\ n+1 \end{pmatrix} f^{(n+1)}(x_0 + \tau_2 h)\right]$$

$$\begin{pmatrix} 0 \le \tau_1 \le n, \\ 0 \le \tau_2 \le n \end{pmatrix}.$$

(Provided $0 \le t \le n$)

The **values of the coefficients** for this formula are shown in Table 3.

TABLE 3

Coefficients for the Stirling Interpolation Formula

t	$\dfrac{t^2}{2!}$	$\dfrac{t(t^2-1)}{3!}$	$\dfrac{t^2(t^2-1)}{4!}$
0,00	+ 0,00000	— 0,0000	— 0,0000
01	00005	0017	0000
02	00020	0033	0000
03	00045	0050	0000
04	00080	0067	0001
0,05	+ 0,00125	— 0,0083	— 0,0001
06	00180	0100	0001
07	00245	0116	0002
08	00320	0133	0003
09	00405	0149	0003
0,10	+ 0,00500	— 0,0165	— 0,0004
11	00605	0181	0005
12	00720	0197	0006
13	00845	0213	0007
14	00980	0229	0008
0,15	+ 0,01125	— 0,0244	— 0,0009
16	01280	0260	0010
17	01445	0275	0012
18	01620	0290	0013
19	01805	0305	0014
0,20	+ 0,02000	— 0,0320	— 0,0016
21	02205	0335	0018
22	02420	0349	0019
23	02645	0363	0021
24	02880	0377	0023
0,25	+ 0,03125	— 0,0391	— 0,0024
26	03380	0,404	0026
27	03645	0417	0028
28	03920	0430	0030
29	04205	0443	0032
0,30	+ 0,04500	— 0,0455	— 0,0034
31	04805	0467	0036
32	05120	0479	0038
33	05445	0490	0040
34	05780	0501	0043
0,35	+ 0,06125	- 0,0512	— 0,0045
36	06480	0522	0047
37	06845	0532	0049
38	07220	0542	0051
39	07605	0551	0054
0,40	+ 0,08000	— 0,0560	— 0,0056
41	08405	0568	0058
42	08820	0576	0060
43	09245	0584	0063
44	09680	0591	0065

Continuation of Table 3

t	$\dfrac{t^2}{2!}$	$\dfrac{t(t^2-1)}{3!}$	$\dfrac{t^2(t^2-1)}{4!}$
0,45	+0,10125	−0,0598	−0,0067
46	10580	0604	0069
47	11045	0610	0072
48	11520	0616	0074
49	12005	0621	0076
0,50	+0,12500	−0,0625	−0,0078

D. Bessel's Formula (Fig. 5)

$$f(x_0 + th) = f_{1/2} + \left(t - \frac{1}{2}\right)f'_{1/2} + \frac{t(t-1)}{2!}f''_{1/2} + \frac{t(t-1)\left(t-\frac{1}{2}\right)}{3!}f'''_{1/2} +$$

$$+ \frac{t(t-2)(t^2-1)}{4!}f^{IV}_{1/2} + \frac{t(t-2)(t^2-1)\left(t-\frac{1}{2}\right)}{5!}f^V_{1/2} + \frac{t(t-3)(t^2-4)(t^2-1)}{6!}f^{VI}_{1/2}\cdots$$

Here even differences with *fractional* index are used; they are regarded as semi-sums of adjacent differences of the same order.

Fig. 5

Remainder:

a) n odd:

$$R_n = \binom{t + \dfrac{n-1}{2}}{n+1} h^{n+1} f^{(n+1)}(x_0 + \tau h) =$$

$$= \frac{t\left(t - \dfrac{n+1}{2}\right)(t^2-1)(t^2-4)\ldots\left(t^2 - \dfrac{(n-1)^2}{4}\right)}{(n+1)!} h^{n+1} f^{(n+1)}(x_0 + \tau h)$$

$$(0 \leqq \tau \leqq n).$$

b) n even (There is no advantage in using the Bessel formula in this case):

$$R_n = \frac{h^{n+1}}{2}\left[\binom{t + \dfrac{n}{2}}{n+1}f^{(n+1)}(x_0 + \tau_1 h) + \binom{t + \dfrac{n-2}{2}}{n+1}f^{(n+1)}(x_0 + \tau_2 h)\right]$$

$$\left(\begin{matrix}0 \leqq \tau_1 \leqq n, \\ 0 \leqq \tau_2 \leqq n\end{matrix}\right).$$

(Provided $0 \leqq t \leqq n$).

The values of the coefficients for this formula are shown in Table 4.[2]

---

[2] To save space, the arguments are given in two columns in this table. The signs applying to the functional values correspond as follows: the one on the left to the lefthand column of arguments, the one on the right to the righthand column.

TABLE 4

Coefficients for the Bessel Interpolation Formula

t	$\dfrac{t(t-1)}{2!}$	$\dfrac{t(t-1)(t-\frac{1}{2})}{3!}$	$\dfrac{t(t-2)(t^2-1)}{4!}$	t
0,00	—0,00000—	+0,0000—	+0,0000+	1,00
01	00495	0008	0008	99
02	00980	0016	0016	98
03	01455	0023	0025	97
04	—0,01920—	+0,0029—	+0,0033+	96
0,05	—0,02375—	+0,0036—	+0,0041+	0,95
06	02820	0041	0048	94
07	03255	0047	0056	93
08	03680	0052	0064	92
09	—0,04095—	+0,0056—	+0,0071+	91
0,10	—0,04500—	+0,0060—	+0,0078+	0,90
11	04895	0064	0086	89
12	05280	0067	0093	88
13	05655	0070	0100	87
14	—0,06020—	+0,0072—	+0,0106+	86
0,15	—0,06375—	+0,0074—	+0,0113+	0,85
16	06720	0076	0120	84
17	07055	0078	0126	83
18	07380	0079	0132	82
19	—0,07695—	+0,0080—	+0,0138+	81
0,20	—0,08000—	+0,0080—	+0,0144+	0,80
21	08295	0080	0150	79
22	08580	0080	0155	78
23	08855	0080	0161	77
24	—0,09120—	+0,0079—	+0,0166+	76
0,25	—0,09375—	+0,0078—	+0,0171+	0,75
26	09620	0077	0176	74
27	09855	0076	0180	73
28	10080	0074	0185	72
29	—0,10295—	+0,0072—	+0,0189+	71
0,30	—0,10500—	+0,0070—	+0,0193+	0,70
31	10695	0068	0197	69
32	10880	0065	0201	68
33	11055	0063	0205	67
34	—0,11220—	+0,0060—	+0,0208+	66
0,35	—0,11375—	+0,0057—	+0,0211+	0,65
36	11520	0054	0214	64
37	11655	0050	0217	63
38	11780	0047	0219	62
39	—0,1189 —	+0,0044—	+0,0222+	61
0,40	—0,12000—	+0,0040—	+0,0224+	0,60
41	12095	0036	0226	59
42	12180	0032	0228	58
43	12255	0029	0229	57
44	—0,12320—	+0,0025—	+0,0231+	56

Continuation of Table 4

t	$\dfrac{t\,(t-1)}{2!}$	$\dfrac{t\,(t-1)\,(t-\frac{1}{2})}{3!}$	$\dfrac{t\,(t-2)\,(t^2-1)}{4!}$	t
0,45	−0,12375 —	+0,0021 —	+0,0232 +	0,55
46	12420	0017	0233	54
47	12455	0012	0233	53
48	12480	0008	0234	52
49	−0,12495	+0,0004 —	+0,0234 +	51
0,50	−0,12500	0,0000	+0,0234 +	0,50

E. Lagrange Formula

All the formulae hitherto cited use differences of given values of functions. In a number of cases it is useful to use the values themselves direct. This can be done with the help of the Lagrange formula.

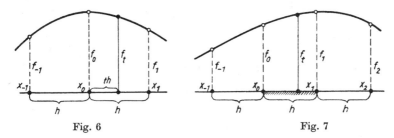

Fig. 6   Fig. 7

a) Three-point interpolation. An intermediate value f_t of a function f, whose values at the points x_0, $x_0 + h$, $x_0 - h$ (Fig. 6) are known, is determined according to the following formula:

$$f(x_0 + th) = A_{-1} f_{-1} + A_0 f_0 + A_1 f_1 \qquad (-1 \leqq t \leqq 1).$$

The coefficients of this formula have the form

$$A_k(t) = (-1)^{k+1} \frac{t\,(t^2-1)}{(1+k)!\,(1-k)!\,(t-k)} \quad (k = 0;\ \pm 1).$$

Their values at intervals of one-hundredth from $t = -1$ to $t = +1$ are shown in Table 5 (p. 14). To save space the coefficients are used simultaneously in this table for t positive and t negative; for t positive the top heading applies, for t negative the designations at the foot.

b) Four-point interpolation. An intermediate value f_t of a function f, whose values at the points x_0, $x_0 - h$, $x_0 + h$, $x_0 + 2h$ (Fig. 7) are known, is determined in accordance with the following formula:

$$f(x_0 + th) = A_{-1} f_{-1} + A_0 f_0 + A_1 f_1 + A_2 f_2.$$

The values t are usually taken from 0 to 1, i.e. they correspond to the interval points from x_0 to $x_1 = x_0 + h$ (shaded in Fig. 7).

The coefficients of this formula have the form

$$A_k(t) = (-1)^{k+2} \frac{t(t^2-1)(t-2)}{(1+k)!(2-k)!(t-k)} \quad (k = 0; \ \pm 1; 2)$$

Their values for each one-hundredth from $t = 0$ to $t = 1$ are given in Table 6. To save space, the arguments appear in two columns in this table; extreme left and extreme right. The symbols for the coefficients pertaining to the lefthand column of arguments are along the top line of the table, those belonging to the righthand column run along the bottom. For more detailed tables of coefficients for the Lagrange formula see [E23].

TABLE 5

Coefficients of the Lagrange Interpolation Formula for n = 3

t	A_{-1}	A_0	A_1
0,00	−0,00000	+1,00000	+0,00000
01	00495	0,99990	00505
02	00980	99960	01020
03	01455	99910	01545
04	01920	99840	02080
0,05	−0,02375	+0,99750	+0,02625
06	02820	99640	03180
07	03255	99510	03745
08	03680	99360	04320
09	04095	99190	04905
0,10	−0,04500	+0,99000	+0,05500
11	04895	98790	06105
12	05280	98560	06720
13	05655	98310	07345
14	06020	98040	07980
0,15	−0,06375	+0,97750	+0,08625
16	06720	97440	09280
17	07055	97110	09945
18	07380	96760	10620
19	07695	96390	11305
0,20	−0,08000	+0,96000	+0,12000
21	08295	95590	12705
22	08580	95160	1 420
23	08855	94710	14145
24	09120	94240	14880
0,25	−0,09375	+0,93750	+0,15625
26	09620	93240	16380
27	09855	92710	17145
28	10080	92160	17920
29	10295	91590	18705
$-t$	A_1	A_0	A_{-1}

Continuation of Table 5

t	A_{-1}	A_0	A_1
0,30	—0,10500	+0,91000	+0,19500
31	10695	90390	20305
32	10880	89760	21120
33	11055	89110	21945
34	11220	88440	22780
0,35	—0,11375	+0,87750	+0,23625
36	11520	87040	24480
37	11655	86310	25345
38	11780	85560	26220
39	11895	84790	27105
0,40	—0,12000	+0,84000	+0,28000
41	12095	83190	28905
42	12180	82350	29820
43	12255	81510	30745
44	12320	80640	31680
0,45	—0,12375	+0,79750	+0,32625
46	12420	78840	33580
47	12455	77910	34545
48	12480	76960	35520
49	12495	75990	36505
0,50	—0,12500	+0,75000	+0,37500
51	12495	73990	38505
52	12480	72960	39520
53	12455	71910	40545
54	12420	70840	41580
0,55	—0,12375	+0,69750	+0,42625
56	12320	68640	43680
57	12255	67510	44745
58	12180	66360	45820
59	12095	65190	46905
0,60	—0,12000	+0,64000	+0,48000
61	11895	62790	49105
62	11780	61560	50220
63	11655	60310	51345
64	11520	59040	52480
0,65	—0,11375	+0,57750	+0,53625
66	11220	56440	54780
67	11055	55110	55945
68	10880	53760	57120
69	10695	52390	58305
0,70	—0,10500	+0,51000	+0,59500
71	10295	49590	60705
72	10080	48160	61920
73	09855	46710	63145
74	09620	45240	64380
—t	A_1	A_0	A_{-1}

Continuation of Table 5

t	A_{-1}	A_0	A_1
0,75	—0,09375	+ 0,43750	+ 0,65625
76	09120	42240	66880
77	08855	40720	68145
78	08580	39170	69420
79	08295	37590	70705
0,80	—0,08000	+ 0,36000	+ 0,72000
81	07695	34390	73305
82	07380	32760	74620
83	07055	31110	75945
84	06720	29440	77280
0,85	—0,06375	+ 0,27750	+ 0,78625
86	06020	26040	79980
87	05655	24310	81345
88	05280	22560	82720
89	04895	20790	84105
0,90	—0,04500	+ 0,19000	+ 0,85500
91	04095	17190	86905
92	03680	15360	88320
93	03255	13510	89745
94	02820	11640	91180
0,95	—0,02375	+ 0,09750	+ 0,92625
96	01920	07840	94080
97	01455	05910	95545
98	00980	03960	97020
99	00495	01990	98505
1,00	—0,00000	+ 0,00000	+ 1,00000
$-t$	A_1	A_0	A_{-1}

TABLE 6

Coefficients of the Lagrange Interpolation Formula for $n = 4$

t	A_{-1}	A_0	A_1	A_2	
0,00	—0,00000	+ 1,00000	+ 0,00000	—0,00000	1,00
01	00328	0,99490	01005	00167	0,99
02	00647	98960	0,2020	00333	98
03	00955	98411	03044	00500	97
04	01254	97843	04077	00666	96
0,05	—0,01544	+ 0,97256	+ 0,05119	—0,00831	0,95
06	01824	96651	06169	00996	94
07	02094	96027	07228	01161	93
08	02355	95386	08294	01325	92
09	02607	94726	09369	01488	91
	A_2	A_1	A_0	A_{-1}	t

Continuation of Table 6

t	A_{-1}	A_0	A_1	A_2	
0,10	—0,02850	+0,94050	+0,10450	—0,01650	0,90
11	03084	93357	11538	01811	89
12	03309	92646	12634	01971	88
13	03525	91920	13735	02130	87
14	03732	91177	14843	02288	86
0,15	—0,03931	+0,90419	+0,15956	—0,02444	0,85
16	04122	89645	17075	02598	84
17	04304	88856	18199	02751	83
18	04477	88052	19328	02903	82
19	0,4643	87233	20462	03052	81
0,20	—0,04800	+0,86400	+0,21600	—0,03200	0,80
21	04949	85553	22742	03346	79
22	05091	84692	23888	03489	78
23	05224	83818	25037	03631	77
24	05350	82931	26189	03770	76
0,25	—0,05469	+0,82031	+0,27344	—0,03906	0,75
:6	05580	81119	28501	04040	74
27	05683	80194	29661	04172	73
28	05779	79258	30822	04301	72
29	05868	78309	31986	04427	71
0,30	—0,05950	+0,77350	+0,33150	—0,04550	0,70
31	06025	76380	34315	04670	69
32	06093	75398	35482	04787	68
33	06154	74407	36648	04901	67
34	06208	73405	37815	05012	66
0,35	—0,06256	+0,72394	+0,38981	—0,05119	0,65
36	06298	71373	40147	05222	64
37	06333	70343	41312	05322	63
38	06361	69304	42476	05419	62
39	06384	68256	43639	05511	61
0,40	—0,06400	+0,67200	+0,44800	—0,05600	0,60
41	06410	66136	459⁚9	05685	59
42	06415.	65064	47116	05765	58
43	06413	63985	48270	05842	57
44	06406	62899	49421	05914	56
0,45	—0,06394	+0,61806	+0,50569	—0,05981	0,55
46	06376	60707	51713	06044	54
47	06352	59601	52854	06103	53
48	06323	58490	53990	06157	52
49	06289	57372	55123	06206	51
0,50	—0,06250	+0,56250	+0,56250	—0,06250	0,50
	A_2	A_1	A_0	A_{-1}	t

2. *Difference Formulae for the Calculation of Derivatives*

A. Derivatives of Functions of One Variable

1. Newton's formula

$$\frac{df}{dx}\bigg|_{x=x_0+th} = \frac{1}{h}\left[f'_{1/_2} + \frac{2t-1}{2!}f''_1 + \frac{3t^2-6t+2}{3!}f''_{3/_2} + \frac{4t^3-18t^2+22t-6}{4!}f_2^{IV} + \cdots\right].$$

2. Stirling's formula

$$\frac{df}{dx}\bigg|_{x=x_0+th} = \frac{1}{h}\left[f'_0 + tf''_0 + \frac{3t^2-1}{3!}f'''_0 + \frac{4t^3-2t}{4!}f_0^{IV} + \frac{5t^4-15t^2+4}{5!}f_0^V + \right.$$
$$\left. + \frac{6t^5-20t^3+8t}{6!}f_0^{VI} + \cdots\right].$$

The *values of the coefficients* of this formula are given in Table 7.

TABLE 7

Coefficients of the Stirling Formula for the Calculation of the Derivative

t	$\dfrac{3t^2-1}{3!}$	$\dfrac{4t^3-2t}{4!}$	$\dfrac{5t^4-15t^2+4}{5!}$	$\dfrac{6t^5-20t^3+8t}{6!}$
0,00	−0,16667	−0,0000	+0,0333	+0,0000
01	16662	0008	0333	0001
02	16647	0017	0333	0002
03	16622	0025	0332	0003
04	16587	0033	0331	0004
0,05	−0,16542	−0,0041	+0,0330	+0,0006
06	16487	0050	0329	0007
07	16422	0058	0327	0008
08	16347	0066	0325	0009
09	16262	0074	0323	0010
0,10	−0,16167	−0,0082	+0,0321	+0,0011
11	16062	0089	0318	0012
12	15947	0097	0315	0013
13	15822	0105	0312	0014
14	15687	0112	0309	0015
0,15	−0 15542	−0,0119	+0,0305	+0,0016
16	15387	0127	0302	0017
17	15222	0133	0298	0018
18	15047	0140	0293	0018
19	14862	0147	0289	0019
0,20	−0,14667	−0,0153	+0,0284	+0,0020
21	14462	0160	0279	0021
22	14247	0166	0274	0022
23	14022	0171	0268	0022
24	13787	0177	0263	0023
0,25	−0,13542	−0,0182	+0,0257	+0,0024

3. Bessel's formula

$$\frac{df}{dx}\bigg|_{x=x_0+th} = \frac{1}{h}\left[f'_{1/_2} + \frac{2t-1}{2} f''_{1/_2} + \frac{6t^2-6t+1}{12} f'''_{1/_2} + \frac{2t^3-3t^2-t+1}{12} f^{IV}_{1/_2} + \right.$$
$$\left. + \frac{5t^4-10t^3+5t-1}{120} f^V_{1/_2} + \cdots \right].$$

The values of the coefficients for this formula are shown in Table 8.
The formulas cited can be used for obtaining higher derivatives, by differentiating them with respect to t and multiplying by $\frac{1}{h}$ $\left(\text{since } \frac{d}{dx} = \frac{1}{h}\frac{d}{dt}\right)$.

Special formulas are obtained from the general ones for $t = 0$. These are shown in Table 9.

TABLE 8

Coefficients of the Bessel Formula for the Calculation of the Derivative

$\dfrac{2t-1}{2}$	$\dfrac{6t^2-6t+1}{12}$	$\dfrac{2t^3-3t^2-t+1}{12}$	$\dfrac{5t^4-10t^3+5t-1}{120}$	$\dfrac{1}{720}[6t^5-15t^4-20t^3+45t^2+8t-12]$
0,00	—0,04167	—0,0000	+0,0047	+0,0000
01	04162	0021	0047	0004
02	04147	0042	0047	0009
03	04122	0062	0046	0013
04	04087	0083	0046	0018
0,05	—0 04042	—0,0104	+0,0045	+0,0022
06	03987	0125	0045	0027
07	03922	0145	0044	0031
08	03847	0166	0043	0036
09	03762	0186	0042	0040
0,10	—0,03667	—0,0207	+0,0041	+0,0044
11	03562	0227	0039	0049
12	03447	0247	0038	0053
13	03322	0267	0036	0057
14	03187	0287	0035	0062
0,15	—0,03042	—0,0307	+0,0033	+0,0066
16	02887	0327	0031	0070
17	02722	0346	0029	0074
18	02547	0365	0027	0078
19	02362	0384	0025	0082
0,20	—0,02167	—0,0403	+0,0023	+0,0086
21	01962	0422	0020	0090
22	01747	0441	0018	0094
23	01522	0459	0015	0098
24	01287	0477	0012	0101
0,25	—0,01042	—0,0495	+0,0009	+0,0105

TABLE 9

Interpolation Formulae for the Calculation of Derivatives

No.	Derivative	Formula	
1	$\dfrac{df}{dx}$	$\dfrac{df}{dx}\Big\|_{x=x_0} = \dfrac{1}{h}\Big[f'_{1/2} - \dfrac{1}{2}f''_1 + \dfrac{1}{3}f'''_{3/2} - \dfrac{1}{4}f^{IV}_2 + \\ \qquad\qquad + \dfrac{1}{5}f^{V}_{5/2} - \dfrac{1}{6}f^{VI}_3 + \cdots\Big]$	Newton
2		$\dfrac{df}{dx}\Big\|_{x=x_0} = \dfrac{1}{h}\Big[f'_0 - \dfrac{1}{6}f'''_0 + \dfrac{1}{30}f^{V}_0 - \dfrac{1}{140}f^{VII}_0 + \cdots\Big]$	Stirling
3		$\dfrac{df}{dx}\Big\|_{x=x_0} = \dfrac{1}{h}\Big[f'_{1/2} - \dfrac{1}{24}f'''_{1/2} + \dfrac{3}{640}f^{V}_{1/2} - \dfrac{5}{7168}f^{VII}_{1/2} + \cdots\Big]$	Bessel
4	$\dfrac{d^2f}{dx^2}$	$\dfrac{d^2f}{dx^2}\Big\|_{x=x_0} = \dfrac{1}{h^2}\Big[f''_1 - f'''_{3/2} + \dfrac{11}{12}f^{IV}_2 - \dfrac{5}{6}f^{V}_{5/2} + \dfrac{137}{180}f^{VI}_3 - \cdots\Big]$	Newton
5		$\dfrac{d^2f}{dx^2}\Big\|_{x=x_0} = \dfrac{1}{h^2}\Big[f''_0 - \dfrac{1}{12}f^{IV}_0 + \dfrac{1}{90}f^{VI}_0 - \dfrac{1}{560}f^{VIII}_0 + \cdots\Big]$	Stirling
6		$\dfrac{d^2f}{dx^2}\Big\|_{x=x_0} = \dfrac{1}{h^2}\Big[f''_{1/2} - \dfrac{5}{24}f^{IV}_{1/2} + \dfrac{259}{5760}f^{VI}_{1/2} - \\ \qquad\qquad - \dfrac{3229}{322560}f^{VIII}_{1/2} + \cdots\Big]$	Bessel
7	$\dfrac{d^3f}{dx^3}$	$\dfrac{d^3f}{dx^3}\Big\|_{x=x_0} = \dfrac{1}{h^3}\Big[f'''_{3/2} - \dfrac{3}{2}f^{IV}_2 + \dfrac{7}{4}f^{V}_{5/2} - \dfrac{15}{8}f^{VI}_3 + \cdots\Big]$	Newton
8		$\dfrac{d^3f}{dx^3}\Big\|_{x=x_0} = \dfrac{1}{h^3}\Big[f'''_0 - \dfrac{1}{4}f^{V}_0 + \dfrac{7}{120}f^{VII}_0 - \cdots\Big]$	Stirling
9		$\dfrac{d^3f}{dx^3}\Big\|_{x=x_0} = \dfrac{1}{h^3}\Big[f'''_{1/2} - \dfrac{1}{8}f^{V}_{1/2} + \dfrac{37}{1920}f^{VII}_{1/2} - \cdots\Big]$	Bessel

Continuation of Table 9

No.	Derivative	Formula	
10	$\dfrac{d^4f}{dx^4}$	$\dfrac{d^4f}{dx^4}\Big|_{x=x_0} = \dfrac{1}{h^4}\left[f_2^{IV} - 2f_{5/2}^{V} + \dfrac{17}{6}f_3^{VI} - \cdots \right]$	Newton
11		$\dfrac{d^4f}{dx^4}\Big|_{x=x_0} = \dfrac{1}{h^4}\left[f_0^{IV} - \dfrac{1}{6}f_0^{VI} + \dfrac{7}{240}f_0^{VIII} - \cdots \right]$	Stirling
12		$\dfrac{d^4f}{dx^4}\Big|_{x=x_0} = \dfrac{1}{h^4}\left[f_{1/2}^{IV} - \dfrac{7}{24}f_{1/2}^{VI} + \dfrac{47}{640}f_{1/2}^{VIII} - \cdots \right]$	Bessel

TABLE 10

Differential Expressions for Partial Derivatives

No.	Derivative	Pattern	Approximate formula
1	$\dfrac{\partial u}{\partial x}$		$\dfrac{\partial u_{ik}}{\partial x} = \dfrac{u_{i+1,k} - u_{i-1,k}}{2h}$
2			$\dfrac{\partial u_{ik}}{\partial x} =$ $= \dfrac{u_{i+1,k+1} - u_{i-1,k+1} + u_{i+1,k-1} - u_{i-1,k-1}}{4h}$
3	$\dfrac{\partial u}{\partial y}$		$\dfrac{\partial u_{ik}}{\partial y} = \dfrac{u_{i,k+1} - u_{i,k-1}}{2l}$
4			$\dfrac{\partial u_{ik}}{\partial y} =$ $= \dfrac{u_{i+1,k+1} - u_{i+1,k-1} + u_{i-1,k+1} - u_{i-1,k-1}}{4l}$

Continuation of Table 10

No.	Derivative	Pattern	Approximate formula
5	$\dfrac{\partial^2 u}{\partial x^2}$		$\dfrac{\partial^2 u_{ik}}{\partial x^2} = \dfrac{1}{h^2}\,(u_{i+1,\,k} - 2u_{ik} + u_{i-1,\,k})$
6			$\dfrac{\partial^2 u_{ik}}{\partial x^2} = \dfrac{1}{12\,h^2}\,(-u_{i+2,\,k} + 16\,u_{i+1,\,k} -$ $- 30\,u_{ik} + 16\,u_{i-1,\,k} - u_{i-2,\,k})$
7			$\dfrac{\partial^2 u_{ik}}{\partial x^2} = \dfrac{1}{3\,h^2}\,(u_{i+1,\,k+1} - 2u_{i,\,k+1} + u_{i-1,\,k+1} +$ $+ u_{i+1,\,k} - 2u_{ik} + u_{i-1,\,k} +$ $+ u_{i+1,\,k-1} - 2u_{i,\,k-1} + u_{i-1,\,k-1})$
8	$\dfrac{\partial^2 u}{\partial y^2}$		$\dfrac{\partial^2 u_{ik}}{\partial y^2} = \dfrac{1}{l^2}\,(u_{i,\,k+1} - 2u_{ik} + u_{i,\,k-1})$
9			$\dfrac{\partial^2 u_{ik}}{\partial y^2} = \dfrac{1}{12\,l^2}\,(-u_{i,\,k+2} + 16\,u_{i,\,k+1} -$ $- 30\,u_{ik} + 16\,u_{i,\,k-1} - u_{i,\,k-2})$
10			$\dfrac{\partial^2 u_{ik}}{\partial y^2} = \dfrac{1}{3\,l^2}\,(u_{i+1,\,k+1} - 2u_{i+1,\,k} + u_{i+1,\,k-1} +$ $+ u_{i,\,k+1} - 2u_{ik} + u_{i,\,k-1} +$ $+ u_{i-1,\,k+1} - 2u_{i-1,\,k} + u_{i-1,\,k-1})$

Continuation of Table 10

No.	Derivative	Pattern	Approximate formula
11	$\dfrac{\partial^2 u}{\partial x \partial y}$		$\dfrac{\partial^2 u_{ik}}{\partial x \partial y} = \dfrac{1}{4hl}\,(u_{i+1,k+1} - u_{i+1,k-1} - \\ - u_{i-1,k+1} + u_{i-1,k-1})$
12			$\dfrac{\partial^2 u_{ik}}{\partial x \partial y} = -\dfrac{1}{2hl}\,(u_{i+1,k} + u_{i-1,k} + u_{i,k+1} + \\ + u_{i,k-1} - 2u_{i,k} - \\ - u_{i+1,k+1} - u_{i-1,k-1})$
13			$\dfrac{\partial^2 u_{ik}}{\partial x \partial y} = \dfrac{1}{2hl}\,(u_{i+1,k} + u_{i-1,k} + u_{i,k+1} + \\ + u_{i,k-1} - 2u_{i,k} - u_{i-1,k+1} - \\ - u_{i+1,k-1})$
14	$\dfrac{\partial^4 u}{\partial x^4}$		$\dfrac{\partial^4 u_{ik}}{\partial x^4} = \dfrac{1}{h^4}\,(u_{i+2,k} - 4u_{i+1,k} + 6u_{i,k} - \\ - 4u_{i-1,k} + u_{i-2,k})$
15	$\dfrac{\partial^4 u}{\partial y^4}$		$\dfrac{\partial^4 u_{ik}}{\partial y^4} = \dfrac{1}{l^4}\,(u_{i,k+2} - 4u_{i,k+1} + 6u_{i,k} - \\ - 4u_{i,k-1} + u_{i,k-2})$
16	$\dfrac{\partial^4 u}{\partial x^2 \partial y^2}$		$\dfrac{\partial^4 u_{ik}}{\partial x^2 \partial y^2} = \dfrac{1}{h^2 l^2}\,(u_{i+1,k+1} + u_{i-1,k+1} + \\ + u_{i+1,k-1} + u_{i-1,k-1} - \\ - 2u_{i+1,k} - 2u_{i-1,k} - \\ - 2u_{i,k+1} - 2u_{i,k-1} + 4u_{i,k})$

B. Partial Derivatives

The formulae for the calculation of partial derivatives are given in a form containing no differences; they are expressed directly by the functional values themselves. The values of the function at the point $(x_0 + ih, y_0 + kl)$ are denoted by u_{ik}:

$$u_{ik} = u(x_0 + ih, y_0 + kl).$$

Pattern-sketches are attached to the formulae to show which functional values (at which points) enter into the formula. The values of all derivatives are taken at the point $(x_0 + ih, y_0 + kl)$. The formulae for the expressions of partial derivatives appear in Table 10.

3. Evaluation of the Accuracy Attainable in the Solution of Partial Differential Equations by the Method of Differences

RUNGE's Principle. It is extraordinarily difficult to estimate the accuracy of approximation that can be attained in the solution of a differential equation by the method of differences using differences corresponding to a given length of interval. Evaluation formulae given by various authors [G51], [R31], [R36], are for the most part rough and, moreover, extremely complicated. Runge's principle permits the problem of estimating the error to be greatly simplified in many cases. This principle is as follows:

We may know that the order of magnitude of the error in a solution with the aid of differences of interval length h is equal to n, i.e. the error $\varepsilon_h(x, y)$ at any point (x, y) can be approximately represented by

$$\varepsilon_h(x, y) \approx k(x, y) h^n,$$

where the function $k(x, y)$ is independent of h.

We may have the approximate solutions $U_{2h}(x, y)$ and $U_h(x, y)$ at the intervals $2h$ and h. If we denote the exact solution by $u(x, y)$, then

$$u(x, y) = U_{2h}(x, y) + \varepsilon_{2h}(x, y),$$
$$u(x, y) = U_h(x, y) + \varepsilon_h(x, y).$$

From which we obtain by subtraction

$$U_h(x, y) - U_{2h}(x, y) = \varepsilon_{2h}(x, y) - \varepsilon_h(x, y),$$

and since
$$\varepsilon_{2h}(x, y) \approx k(x, y) 2^n h^n \approx 2^n \varepsilon_h(x, y)$$

it follows that
$$U_h(x, y) - U_{2h}(x, y) \approx \varepsilon_h(x, y) [2^n - 1]$$

whence
$$\varepsilon_h(x, y) \approx \frac{U_h(x, y) - U_{2h}(x, y)}{2^n - 1}.$$

This formula yields the following rule for an approximate estimate of the value of the error in the solution by differences with interval length h.

Take the differences in the solutions at corresponding points at interval h and at interval 2h. If these differences are divided by $2^n - 1$, where n is the order of error, they then give approximately the absolute error of the solution for the interval h.

In the solution of the Laplace equation

$$\frac{\partial^2 u}{\partial x^2} + \frac{\partial^2 u}{\partial y^2} = 0$$

and the Poisson equation

$$\frac{\partial^2 u}{\partial x^2} + \frac{\partial^2 u}{\partial y^2} = f(x, y)$$

the error will have the order of magnitude h^2 in a quadratic net of interval length h (on correcting the boundary value as suggested by COLLATZ), and this means it will be approximately equal to one third of the difference between the solutions at the intervals h and $2h$.

III. LAPLACE AND POISSON EQUATIONS

1. *General Introduction*

Choice of Network and Construction of Network Field

The first question to arise in the approximate solution of a boundary value problem is with regard to the network field that takes the place of the given field when carrying out the solution. This question falls into two parts: the choice of lateral dimension for the squares of which the network consists, and the plotting of the network region.

a) The magnitude of a square is theoretically determined by the requirement that the size of the remainder term in the formulas, that are used for the approximate substitution of the differential equation by a difference equation, is smaller than the error allowed in the solution.

In practice, however, such a method is impractical in most cases, since it is impossible to compute the size of the remainder term accurately, and when using an approximation calculus, this size is usually so highly overestimated, that the dimension of the square thus obtained turns out to be too small. It is evident, that with extremely small squares, their quantity will be so large that the solution is not accomplishable in practice. Therefore, another method is more practical. First of all, the problem is solved for a small number of squares, whose dimension is determined by inspection in such a way that there are not less than *two* rows of squares in each part. After the problem is solved in this crude network, one proceeds to a more exact solution by refinement of the network either over the whole domain or in some part of it. The refinement of the network is most conveniently undertaken in such a way that the sides of the squares are chosen half the size of those already used. If the accuracy attained is still not satisfactory, then the refinement is repeated, and so on.

Example. Fig. 8 represents *the plotting of a network* of the type described. In Fig. 8a, the crude network plotted contains *only two rows of squares in the narrowest parts of the domain.* In Fig. 8b, the network is refined by subdividing each square into four new ones. In Fig. 8c, the network is again refined at the reentrant corners of the boundary; at these points the function required usually changes more strongly, and therefore squares of the smallest size must be chosen here.

b) Construction of the Network Field. In the construction of the network field its boundary should be so chosen, that it approximates the boundary of the given field as closely as possible. In every case, the network field must be so chosen that the boundary of the given field always cuts the lines of the network *between a boundary point and an interior point*, and not between two interior points.

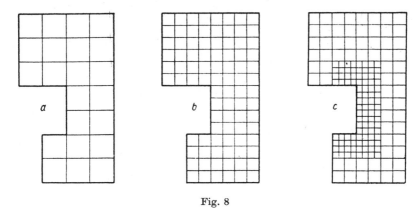

Fig. 8

Example. Fig. 9 *shows the construction of a network* that approximates a circular domain. *In* Fig. 9a *this construction* is carried out in conformity with the above stated requirements. In Fig. 9b, this requirement is not fulfilled. The points in which the

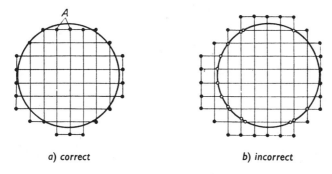

a) correct   b) incorrect

Fig. 9

circle cuts the network between two *interior points* are indicated by white dots.

Note. The boundary points of the network field can lie on the outside just as well as in the interior of the field to be approximated. In Fig. 9a the *points A* lie inside the circular field.

In the *construction of the network* field, which in the long run is the same as the *construction of the boundary* of this field, attention must be paid to the fact that from time to time *some boundary points* (in Fig. 10 the *points* α) have no bearing on the solution of the problem. In fact there are no interior points near the points α, and the values of the function at these points generally play no part in the computations, if one proceeds according to Formula 1 of Table 11 (page 33).

Networks of a different Type (*nonquadratic*)

In many cases the boundary of a given field can be accurately represented if one dispenses with a square network. If a crude network (with a small number of *lattice points*)

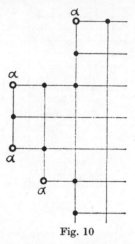

Fig. 10

suffices for the solution of the problem, or if the problem can be solved graphically (the required accuracy being such that the relative error may reach 6—8%) then the use of nonquadratic networks is often of advantage. These networks (rectangular, triangular, or oblique) lead to more intricate equations than does a square network; if there are, however, only a few equations, this circumstance does not unduly overburden the computation, and a solution is possible in such networks.

Example 1. Fig. 11 *illustrates a rectangle with sides in the proportion* 5:11. The required degree of accuracy may be such that for the solution it will be sufficient to use *a network of eight squares*. If, however, it is necessary to use a square network, the field of eight squares has a contour that *does not coincide with the boundary of the given rectangle* (Fig. 11a), and *at point A the value on the boundary must be computed by interpolation*. This can be avoided if smaller squares are taken; however, their number

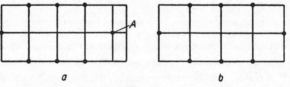

a   *b*

Fig. 11

then increases from 8 to 55, which obviously is no advantage. It is expedient here to take a *rectangular network*, that can be obtained by dividing the long side into four and the short side into two parts (Fig. 11b).

Example 2. Fig. 12 represents a complicated boundary. Fig. 12a gives an approximation by a square network, Fig. 12b by a combination of networks of different appearance (rectangles, triangles, parallelograms).

In the second case, the network boundary coincides exactly with the given boundary, and no interpolation of any kind is necessary when looking for the boundary values in the network. In Fig. 12b, white dots A are marked on the network besides the black points B. These are interior points at which the values must be determined by special devices.

In order to note down the equations for these points, one of the networks must be continued into the interior of the other (in Fig. 12b, the square network is carried on into the interior of the parallelogrammatic network). The values at the points A are then determined by the values at points C, and the values at these points have to be determined by means of interpolation from those values that are obtained at the lattice points of the parallelogram network.

It is to be noted that when using parallelogram and triangular networks, some of such points as the points α in Fig. 10 turn out to be necessary for the solution. Such points are indicated in Fig. 12b by the letters B.

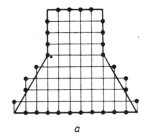 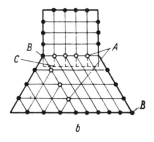

Fig. 12

Formulas for Effecting Computations
with Nonquadratic Networks

The formulas given below refer throughout to the solution of the Poisson equation

$$\frac{\partial^2 u}{\partial x^2} + \frac{\partial^2 u}{\partial y^2} = f(x, y)$$

U_i, f_i denote the values of the functions u and f at the points bearing the number i in the illustration.

The units for the meshes of the network are clearly seen from the illustrations. Moreover, the following notations are established:

$$s_1 = \frac{1}{2}(u_1 + u_4),$$

$$s_2 = \frac{1}{2}(u_2 + u_5),$$

$$s_3 = \frac{1}{2}(u_3 + u_6).$$

1. *Rectangular network* (Fig. 13).

$$u_0 = \frac{a^2(u_1 + u_3) + b^2(u_2 + u_4) - a^2 b^2 f_0}{2(a^2 + b^2)}.$$

In the particular case $a = b$ (square network), we have

$$u_0 = \frac{u_1 + u_3 + u_2 + u_4}{4} - \frac{a^2 f_0}{4}.$$

For $f = 0$ (Laplace Equation),

$$u_0 = \frac{1}{4}(u_1 + u_3 + u_2 + u_4).$$

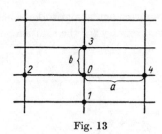

Fig. 13   Fig. 14

2. *Oblique network* (Fig. 14).

$$u_0 = \frac{\lambda_1 s_1 + \lambda_2 s_2 + \lambda_3 s_3}{\lambda_1 + \lambda_2 + \lambda_3} - \frac{f_0 \sin^2 \varphi}{2(\lambda_1 + \lambda_2 + \lambda_0)};$$

$$\lambda_1 = \frac{1}{b^2} - \frac{\cos \varphi}{ab},$$

$$\lambda_2 = \frac{1}{a^2} - \frac{\cos \varphi}{ab},$$

$$\lambda_3 = \frac{\cos \varphi}{ab}.$$

For $\varphi = \frac{\pi}{2}$, the formulas transform into those of Section 1.

3. *Triangular network* (Fig. 15).

The formulas read exactly the same as for the oblique network in Section 2.

4. *Equilateral triangular network* (Fig. 16).

$$u_0 = \frac{S_1 + S_2 + S_3}{3} - \frac{f_0 a^2}{4} = \frac{u_1 + u_2 + u_3 + u_4 + u_5 + u_6}{6} - \frac{f_0 a^2}{4}.$$

This case can be obtained from the general formula of Section 2 for $a = b$, $\varphi = \frac{\pi}{3}$.

Commencement of the Computation and Refinement of the Network

In order to begin the computation according to the method of iteration, the initial distribution of the values of the function in the interior of the field G must be assumed.

The closer these values are to the actual ones, the quicker will the process converge. Hence, it is important to make a favorable choice of initial distribution. This can occur in two ways:

a) graphic, b) numerical.

a) *Graphic Method.* The graphic method is employed in cases where the final result does not require very great accuracy (3 places). The given field is plotted axonometrically (Fig. 17).

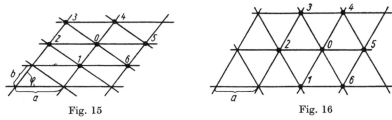

Fig. 15   Fig. 16

The given values of the function are laid off vertically on its boundary. Next, a surface representing the required function is passed freehand through the plotted space curve (more correctly: its intersections with the coordinate planes y, z and x, z are plotted). A rough idea of the form of this surface can be obtained, if one imagines a membrane (e.g. a soap film) stretched onto curve K (Fig. 17). This curve can not

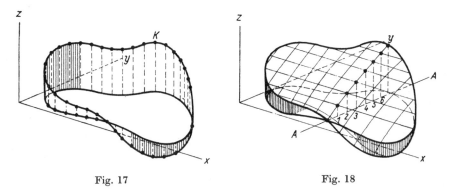

Fig. 17   Fig. 18

contain in the interior of the field any points lying higher than the maximal or lower than the minimal points of curve K. Each intersection must result in as smooth a curve as possible. If the surface is plotted (Fig. 18), the coordinates of each section are read off directly from the drawing; their sizes are taken (on the scale to which the boundary values are plotted) as a first approximation. Fig. 18, for instance, shows how the functional values are found for points 1, 2, 3, . . . , lying on the straight line AA. This graphic method is quite appropriate for the transfer of functional values from the boundary of G to the boundary of $\bar{G}$.

In cases where no great accuracy is required, the whole solution can be carried out graphically.

b) *Numerical Method.* This method consists essentially in a provisional solution of the problem with a small number of squares. In cases requiring great accuracy (4 to 5 places), a large number of squares must also be taken (otherwise the error becomes too large, owing to the substitution of the given field G by the network field $\bar{G}$ and of the derivatives by differences). There is no advantage in carrying out the computations just with a large number of squares and not sufficiently good initial values. Hence, initial values are figured out as accurately as possible, before beginning the computation with a templet or traverse for a large number of squares. This is done as follows: first, the initial values are determined more precisely in the shaded squares of the templet (Fig. 19). Obviously, this is equivalent to one solution of the problem with a templet containing only a quarter of the squares. This solution is determined to three places and the initial distribution is determined graphically.

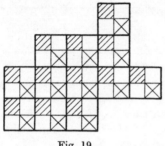

| Fig. 19 | Fig. 20 |

When the solution is found, the initial values are determined for all the remaining squares, first of all for those marked with a cross, next for the blank squares. The values at the points marked with a cross are found by forming the arithmetic mean of the four diagonally adjacent values, according to the formula

$$\varphi_x = \frac{1}{4}\left(\varphi_I + \varphi_{II} + \varphi_{III} + \varphi_{IV}\right)$$

(see Fig. 20), which is sufficient on the basis of Gershgorin's results (R29), and, for filling out the blank squares, the arithmetic mean is taken from the function values in the shaded squares plus the values found in the squares marked with crosses.[3]

In this way the initial values in all squares of the large templet are found with sufficient accuracy, and they guarantee a good convergence of the process. With these values, the ordinary iteration process is continued to the full number (4—5) of places.

The most usual formula for the solution of the Laplace and Poisson equations. The formulas customarily used for the solution of the Laplace and Poisson equations are given below: the network is assumed to be square. Consider the equation

$$\frac{\partial^2 u}{\partial x^2} + \frac{\partial^2 u}{\partial y^2} = f(x, y).$$

The functional values of u and f are denoted by u_i, f_i at the point bearing the number i

---

[3] All this is justified for the solution of the Laplace equation. For the solution of the Poisson equation, formulas 2 and 1 of Table 11 must be taken.

in the pattern. Let the sides of the network squares be equal to h. The formulae for the solution of the Laplace and Poisson equations are shown in Table 11.

TABLE 11

Formulas for the Solution of the Laplace and Poisson Equations

No.	Pattern	Formula	Order of Error
1		$u_0 = \dfrac{1}{4} (u_1 + u_2 + u_3 + u_4) - \dfrac{h^2 f_0}{2}$	h^2
2		$u_0 = \dfrac{1}{4} (u_5 + u_6 + u_7 + u_8) - \dfrac{h^2 f_0}{2}$	h^2
3		$u_0 = \dfrac{4\,[u_1 + u_2 + u_3 + u_4] + [u_5 + u_6 + u_7 + u_8]}{20}$ $- \dfrac{6}{20}\, h^2 f_0$	h^4
4		$u_0 =$ $= \dfrac{16[u_1 + u_2 + u_3 + u_4] - [u_9 + u_{10} + u_{11} + u_{12}]}{60} -$ $- \dfrac{12}{60}\, h^2 f_0$	h^4

2. *The Dirichlet Problem*

Dirichlet's Problem or the first boundary value problem consists, as is well known, in the determination of a function that satisfies the Laplace or Poisson differential equation in the interior of a given domain and has the prescribed values on the boundary of the domain. The solution of this problem by the method of differences is described below.

Computation array. We consider in detail below computation by Formula 1 of Table 11, which is the one most frequently used.

For practical performance of the computation by the iteration process, it is necessary to make ready beforehand a sufficient quantity (10—20) of special computation templets. The type of preparation is shown below. The domain G for which the Dirichlet problem has to be solved, is covered with a network. The function values required are at the lattice points inside the domain $\bar{G}$, which takes the place of domain G in our approximate solution. These lattice points are indicated by white circles in Fig. 21a.

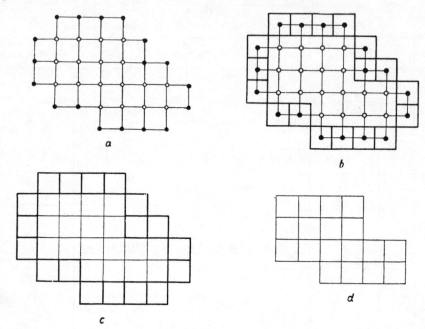

Fig. 21 a, b, c, d

At the points lying on the boundary of this domain (indicated by black circles in Fig. 21a) the function values must be known. They are determined by interpolation from those values possessed by the required function with the nearest boundary points of domain G. For the construction of the computation templet, we provide a second network of the same dimensions as the first, but such that its lines run through the middle of the lines on the first. The lattice points of the first network lie inside the squares of the second network (Fig. 21b). We edge the squares of the new network, within which lie the black circles, with a thick black line. When the necessary squares are all edged, the computation templet is ready (Fig. 21c). The outside row of figures is edged in thick lines; in these squares, the edged preassigned function values on the boundary of domain $\bar{G}$ are inscribed; in each square is written the value corresponding to the point in the middle of the field (Fig. 21b). The interior squares are filled out step by step by the iteration process. For this purpose 10—20 templets are prepared, comprising only interior squares (Fig. 21d) of the same size as the squares in the templet of Fig. 21c (such a templet is necessary only once). The given boundary values are written down in the thick bordered squares of templet 1 (Fig. 21c), and the interior squares are filled in with arbitrary values which are taken as a first approximation. After templet 1, the filling out of templet 2 (without outer squares) is proceeded to; in each square, beneath the number n of templet 2, the arithmetic mean of the four numbers in the squares adjacent to square n of templet 1 is written.

The given boundary values are likewise concerned in the composition of these arithmetic means (for those squares abutting on the boundary). When templet 2 is filled out (the templet numbers are written on the back), it is laid on top of templet 1 (the boundary values remaining uncovered, since templet 2 contains only interior squares) and templet 3 is filled out, while the arithmetic mean is formed from the numbers of templet 2 in the same way as when templet 2 was filled up from the numbers of templet 1. The process is repeated until the values, within the given limits of accuracy, coincide in two successive templets.

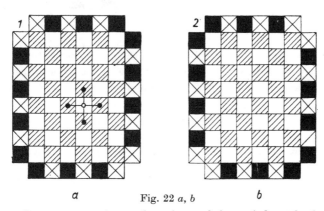

Fig. 22 a, b

Cross Array. In many cases (e.g., when the work is carried out by less competent computers) it is convenient to employ a somewhat different arrangement, the so-called *cross array*. In this, the computation proceeds thus:

With the aid of the values, standing in the shaded squares of templet 1 (Fig. 22a) and the boundary values standing in the black squares, the values in the blank squares will be determined by forming the arithmetic means from four adjacent squares. When all these values have been found, then with their help, fresh values in the shaded squares are obtained, which are shown white in templet 2 (Fig. 22b). After they have been found, the calculation is again worked out with templet 1, then with templet 2, and so on. Fig. 22 shows the templets for the computation by Formula 1 of Table 11. In these templets, a cross (X) indicates those boundary values that do not enter into the computation according to the given templet, but are in fact used in the computation by the succeeding templet.

Fig. 23 shows templets for the computation according to the cross array using Formula 2 of Table 11. In this case certain squares, marked with an asterisk (*) in the templet, do not generally enter into the computations when the array is followed to the letter. In order to bring these squares also into the computation, either Formula 1 and Formula 2 must be used simultaneously or, if Formula 2 is used by itself, the templet must be moved forward by one row after the cycle of calculation has been performed with both of the templets 1 and 2.

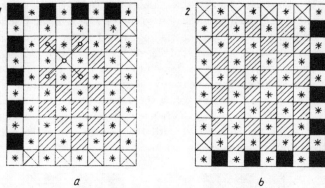

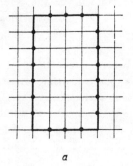

Fig. 23 *a, b*

Improvement of the Values on the Boundary. In those cases where the boundary of the network field coincides with the boundary of the domain for which the Dirichlet problem is to be solved, the values of the required function *u* on the border of the network field are unchanged in the course of the computation (Fig. 24a). In those cases, however, where the boundaries of the network field originally given and of the approximating network field do not coincide (Fig. 24b) this is no longer true. Actually, the values at the points 1, 2, 3, . . . of the network boundary must be given, despite the fact that the values at other points 1′, 2′, 3′, . . . , that is to say on the boundary of domain *G*, are known. For the solution of the Dirichlet problem in the network, the values must be transferred from the boundary points of domain *G* on to the boundary of the network field, and in fact in such a way that after determination of the solution, the function values of *u* on the boundary of domain *G* coincide with those values that were given on the boundary. It is clear that this operation cannot be accurately performed without a knowledge of the function values of *u* in the interior of the domain. As this function is directly required in the solution of the Dirichlet problem, the fulfillment of the conditions on the boundary of *G* can be attained only with the aid of successive approximations. L. Collatz gives an extremely practical method for the improvement of boundary values in this case (G47). This method relates to the use of the formulas given in Table 12.

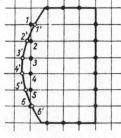

Fig. 24

TABLE 12

Collatz Formulas for Improvement of Boundary Values

Pattern	Equation	Note
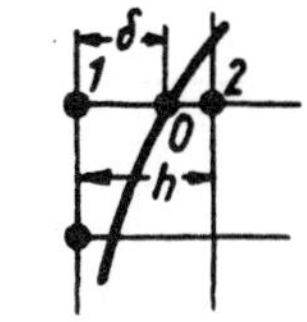	$$u_1 = \frac{h\varphi_0 - \delta u_2}{h - \delta}$$ $$u_1 = \frac{h\varphi_0 + \delta u_2}{h + \delta}$$	In these formulas u_1 denotes the magnitude of function u at point 1 of the array; φ_0 denotes the prescribed value u at point 0 on the G boundary.

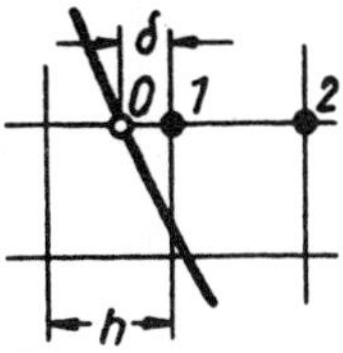

The order of magnitude of error on improvement of boundary values by Collatz' formula is h^2. Essentially more accurate formulas are established in a treatise by MIKELADZE (R37). As not merely one interior value but *three* are used for the improvement of the boundary values, the order of magnitude of error obtained is h^3. Some of these formulas are cited in Table 13.

Refinement of Convergence

a) *Utilization of the Values Just Found.* In order to improve the convergence of the iteration process, we can apply a device that is often used in the solution of sets of equations by the iteration method, namely: In computing the arithmetic mean, not only the values of the previous approximation are used but also those newly found. For instance, the computation of the value in square no. 23 (Fig. 25) of templet 2 can

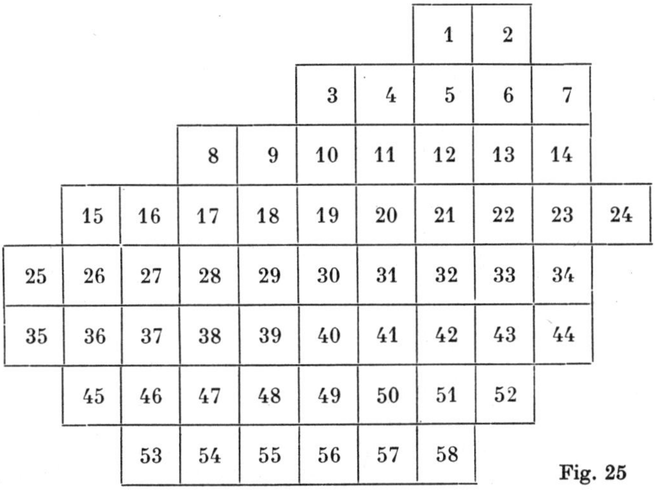

Fig. 25

TABLE 13

Mikeladze Formulas for Improvement of Boundary Values

No.	Pattern	Formula	Magnitude of Error
1		$u_0 = \dfrac{2h^2\varphi_2 + 2h\delta u_4 + \delta(h+\delta)(u_1+u_3)}{(h+\delta)[2h+2\delta+\delta h^2 g_0]} - \dfrac{\delta h^2 f_0}{2h+2\delta+\delta h^2 g_0}\;^{1)}$	
2		$u_0 = \dfrac{h}{h+\delta}\,\dfrac{h\varphi_2+\delta u_4}{h+\delta} + \dfrac{\delta}{h+\delta}\,\dfrac{u_1+u_3}{2} - \dfrac{\delta h^2 f_0}{2(h+\delta)}\;^{2)}$	h^3
3		$u_0 =$ $= \dfrac{2h\varepsilon(h+\varepsilon)\varphi_2 + 2h\delta(h+\delta)\varphi_3 + 2\delta\varepsilon(h+\varepsilon)u_4 + 2\delta\varepsilon(h+\delta)u_1}{(h+\delta)(h+\varepsilon)[2\varepsilon+2\delta+\varepsilon\delta h g_0]} -$ $- \dfrac{\delta\varepsilon h f_0}{2\varepsilon+2\delta+\delta\varepsilon h g_0}\;)$	
4		$u_0 = \dfrac{\varepsilon}{\varepsilon+\delta}\,\dfrac{h\varphi_2+\delta u_4}{h+\delta} + \dfrac{\delta}{\varepsilon+\delta}\,\dfrac{h\varphi_3+\varepsilon u_1}{h+\varepsilon} - \dfrac{\delta\varepsilon h f_0}{2(\varepsilon+\delta)}\;^{2)}$	h^3
5		$u_0 = \dfrac{\delta'}{\delta+\delta'}\,\dfrac{h\varphi_5+\delta u_7}{h+\delta} + \dfrac{\delta}{\delta+\delta'}\,\dfrac{h\varphi_6+\delta' u_8}{h+\delta'} - \dfrac{h\delta\delta'}{\delta+\delta'}\,f_0\;^{2)}$ for the cross array	h^3

---

[4] The formulas relate to the equation

$$\frac{\partial^2 u}{\partial x^2} + \frac{\partial^2 u}{\partial y^2} = g(x,y)\,u + f(x,y).$$

In the case of the Poisson equation, make $g \equiv 0$.

[5] The formula is canceled down to the Poisson equation.

be effected in two ways: Take the arithmetic mean of squares 14, 22, 24, 34 of templet 1 or nos. 34 and 24 of templet 1 and nos. 14 and 22 of templet 2, as they had been determined before the computation of square no. 23. Obviously computation by the second variant attains the purpose more quickly. An expert calculator will find other similar possibilities for accelerating the convergence process in any particular case.

Nevertheless, it must be remembered that the process can be regarded as finished only when agreement within the given limits of accuracy occurs in two successive templets that have been obtained in this order of accuracy by the arithmetic mean method without the devices mentioned in this section. Therefore, the final check is made in accordance with the original array.

b) *Orr's Method of Computation of Correction.* Orr in his paper dealing with torsion in bars (E17) suggests the following method for speeding up the convergence process. When using the cross array, we will denote each arithmetical operation by means of the two templets 1 and 2 as a *cycle.* Let U_0 be an approximate solution at point 0, u_0 the exact solution, U_0' the approximate solution obtained from U_0 after one cycle. Then clearly

$$u_0 = U_0 + \varepsilon_0, \qquad u_0 = U_0' + \varepsilon_0',$$

where the error ε_0' is found from the formula

$$\varepsilon_0' = \frac{1}{4} (\varepsilon_1 + \varepsilon_2 + \varepsilon_3 + \varepsilon_4)$$

ε_i is the value of the error ε at the point situated near point 0 and designated by the number i (Fig. 26).

Regarding the error ε as a function of x and y, we may write:

$$\varepsilon_1 \approx \varepsilon_0 - h \frac{\partial \varepsilon_0}{\partial y} + \frac{1}{2} \left(h^2 \frac{\partial^2 \varepsilon_0}{\partial y^2} \right), \qquad \varepsilon_2 \approx \varepsilon_0 - h \frac{\partial \varepsilon_0}{\partial x} + \frac{1}{2} \left(h^2 \frac{\partial^2 \varepsilon_0}{\partial x^2} \right),$$

$$\varepsilon_3 \approx \varepsilon_0 + h \frac{\partial \varepsilon_0}{\partial y} + \frac{1}{2} \left(h^2 \frac{\partial^2 \varepsilon_0}{\partial y^2} \right), \qquad \varepsilon_4 \approx \varepsilon_0 + h \frac{\partial \varepsilon_0}{\partial x} + \frac{1}{2} \left(h^2 \frac{\partial^2 \varepsilon_0}{\partial x^2} \right).$$

Fig. 26

Whence it follows that

$$\varepsilon_0' \approx \varepsilon_0 + \frac{h^2}{4} \Delta \varepsilon_0,$$

where Δ is the Laplacian operator

$$\Delta = \frac{\partial^2}{\partial x^2} + \frac{\partial^2}{\partial y^2}.$$

On the other hand

$$\varepsilon_0' - \varepsilon_0 = U_0 - U_0'$$

and consequently

$$U_0 - U_0' \approx \frac{h^2}{4} \Delta \varepsilon_0.$$

If we consider the rectangle with sides 2 mh and 2 nh (Fig. 27), on whose boundary the function values u are so given that $\varepsilon = 0$ there, then a favorable approximate expression is given in many cases by

$$\varepsilon (x, y) = \varepsilon_0 \left(1 - \frac{x^2}{m^2 h^2} \right) \left(1 - \frac{y^2}{n^2 h^2} \right).$$

For this function

$$\frac{h^2}{4}\,\Delta\varepsilon = -\frac{1}{2}\,\varepsilon_0\left(\frac{1}{m^2}+\frac{1}{n^2}-\frac{x^2+y^2}{m^2\,n^2\,h^2}\right),\tag{5}$$

and thus, assuming that the error is approximately given by equation (5), we get:

$$\varepsilon_0 \approx -\frac{2(U_0-U_0')}{\dfrac{1}{m^2}+\dfrac{1}{n^2}}=\frac{2(U_0'-U_0)}{\dfrac{1}{m_2}+\dfrac{1}{n^2}}.\tag{6}$$

James Orr proceeding from these considerations suggests taking the formula indicated for the approximation of ϵ and obtaining a closer approximation by adding ϵ to U. If the actual distribution of error lies near to that given by Formula (5), it is evident that this method must greatly facilitate the solution procedure, since values near to the final ones are obtained instantly.

If the boundary of the domain is not a rectangle, it is suggested to substitute for it an equivalent rectangle (see, for instance, Fig. 28), chosen in such a way that on a large part of its boundary the errors are very close to zero. This method can also be utilized for a part of the domain, if a rectangle can be divided off there, such that the errors on its boundary are practically zero.

As the distribution of error generally differs from that given in formula (5), Orr proposes using another formula, as shown in Table 14, which differs from the theoretic formula (6) by an empirically determined coefficient.

c) *Lyusternik's Method of Computing Corrections.* The formula obtained by L. A. LYUSTERNIK in paper [R34] reads:

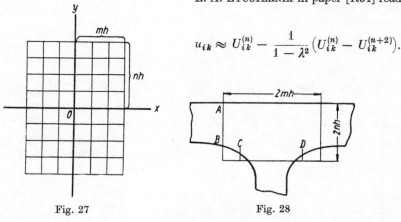

$$u_{ik} \approx U_{ik}^{(n)} - \frac{1}{1-\lambda^2}\left(U_{ik}^{(n)} - U_{ik}^{(n+2)}\right).$$

Fig. 27   Fig. 28

Here u_{ik} denotes the exact solution, $U_{ik}^{(n)}$ denotes an approximate solution obtained after n steps, and λ is the eigenvalue of the problem computed from the approximation equation

$$1+\lambda^2 = \frac{\sum\left(U_{ik}^{(n)}-U_{ik}^{(n+4)}\right)}{\sum\left(U_{ik}^{(n)}-U_{ik}^{(n+2)}\right)}$$

The summation extends over all the interior points of the domain. The computation

of corrections by Lyusternik's method can considerably reduce the number of iterations necessary for solution of the problem.

TABLE 14

Formulas for Computation of Corrections by Use of Cross Arrays

Pattern	Sequential Formula	1 Correction formula in the case of a ₃ rectangle of sides 2 mh and 2 nh
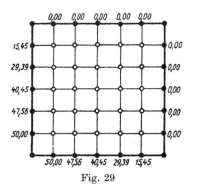	$$U_0 = \frac{1}{4}[U_1+U_2+U_3+U_4]$$	$$\varepsilon_0 \approx \frac{2\,(U_0' - U_0)}{\dfrac{1}{m^2}+\dfrac{1}{n^2}} {}^{1)}$$ U_0' denotes the value of U at point 0 after one cycle.
	$$U_0 = \frac{1}{4}[U_5+U_6+U_7+U_8]$$	$$\varepsilon_0 \approx \frac{1{,}5\,(U_0' - U_0)}{\dfrac{1}{m^2}+\dfrac{1}{n^2}} {}^{2)}$$

Examples for the Solution of the Dirichlet Problem

Example 1. It is required to solve the Laplace equation for a square with the
boundary values shown in Fig. 29. The computation templet for the solution is shown
in Fig. 30. Figure 31 shows the complete solution by means of the iteration process by
Formula 1 of Table 11, in which no use is made of any device for improving the con-

Fig. 29

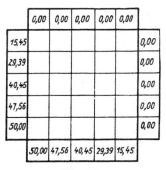

Fig. 30

---

[6] Theoretic formula
[7] Coefficient 1.5 proposed by Orr, instead of the theoretical 1.0.

vergence process. In Fig. 31.1 the initial approximation is given; the remaining tables are only half filled in, in view of their symmetry. Fig. 32 gives the final solution.

The use of Lyusternik's corrections allows a substantial decrease in the number of iterations necessary in this example (R34). To use Lyusternik's formula, three approximations must be taken, always skipping over one; let us take $n = 7, 9, 11$. Among the individual tables of illustration 31, the values of the differences $U_{ik}^{(7)} - U_{ik}^{(9)}$ and $U_{ik}^{(7)} - U_{ik}^{(11)}$ (Tables 7—9, and 7—11, page 44) can be obtained. The calculation of the sums gives:

$$\Sigma\left(U_{ik}^{(7)} - U_{ik}^{(9)}\right) = 2\,(0{,}07 + 0{,}12 + 0{,}12 + 0{,}10 + 0{,}12 + 0{,}21 + 0{,}22 + 0{,}16 +$$
$$+\,0{,}25 + 0{,}14) + 0{,}006 + 0{,}18 + 0{,}27 + 0{,}24 + 0{,}08 = 3{,}85.$$
$$\Sigma\left(U_{ik}^{(7)} - U_{ik}^{(11)}\right) = 2\,(0{,}12 + 0{,}20 + 0{,}22 + 0{,}17 + 0{,}21 + 0{,}36 + 0{,}39 + 0{,}27 +$$
$$+\,0{,}43 + 0{,}24) + 0{,}10 + 0{,}33 + 0{,}48 + 0{,}41 + 0{,}14 = 6{,}68.$$

Then by Lyusternik's formula

$$1 + \lambda^2 = \frac{6{,}68}{3{,}85} = 1{,}735$$

and hence

$$1 - \lambda^2 = 2 - 1{,}735 = 0{,}265;$$
$$\frac{1}{1 - \lambda^2} = \frac{1}{0{,}265} = 3{,}77.$$

Table A of Fig. 31 gives the values

$$U_{ik}^{(7)} - 3{,}77\left(U_{ik}^{(7)} - U_{ik}^{(9)}\right)$$

and Table B gives the arithmetic means. The values obtained correspond to the 26th iteration. Thus Lyusternik's correction computation is equivalent to 14 iterations.

Example 2. Evaluation of Error by Means of Runge's Principle. In Fig. 34 the Dirichlet problem is solved for the Laplace equation for a network field shown in Fig. 33. This is a square of 10×10 small squares. The error in the solution obtained is to be evaluated by means of Runge's principle. For this purpose we solve the problem anew for a square of 5×5 small squares (Fig. 35) by taking every alternate lattice point of the large square, as shown in the pattern of Fig. 36. The solution of this problem is completely carried out in Fig. 37. Fig. 37,1 gives the initial values taken from the heavy-lined squares of Fig. 38. Fig. 37,6 gives the final solution which should be compared with the figures standing in the heavy bordered squares of Fig. 38. The differences of the figures standing in the corresponding fields are given in Fig. 39. Finally, in Fig. 40 the approximate errors in the solution for the 10×10 square (Fig. 34) are to be found, computed according to the formula

$$\varepsilon_h \approx \frac{1}{3}\,(U_h - U_{2h}).$$

Example 3 ([E17], p. 6). *Use of Orr's Corrections.* The torsion problem for a $16'' \times 6''$ H girder is to be solved. The torsion problem, as is well-known, is equivalent to the solution of the Poisson equation with vanishing boundary values.[8]

$$\frac{\partial^2 u}{\partial x^2} + \frac{\partial^2 u}{\partial y^2} + 2 = 0$$

The solution is effected in accordance with the cross array, using Formula 2 of Table 11 with refinement of boundary values; h is made equal to unity. Fig. 41a is an enlarged reproduction of the square lined-in at the top of Fig. 41. In this square the computation of the corrections by Orr's method is shown.[9]

1

12,88	10,30	7,72	5,15	2,58
24,54	19,69	14,85	10,00	5,15
34,05	27,65	21,25	14,85	7,72
40,92	34,29	27,65	19,69	10,30
45,46	40,92	34,05	24,54	12,88

2

12,57	10,07	7,58	5,08	2,58
24,00	19,34	14,66	10,00	
33,39	27,32	21,25		
40,34	34,28			
45,46				

3

12,38	9,87	7,45	5,04	2,54
23,67	19,01	14,54	9,87	
33,03	27,06	20,99		
40,17	33,83			
45,17				

4

12,25	9,71	7,36	4,96	2,52
23,45	18,78	14,33	9,79	
32,84	26,72	20,80		
39,90	33,62			
45,08				

5

12,15	9,60	7,25	4,92	2,48
23,32	18,55	14,18	9,64	
32,63	26,41	20,52		
39,78	33,31			
44,95				

6

12,09	9,49	7,18	4,84	2,46
23,18	18,40	13,99	9,55	
32,52	26,25	20,34		
39,61	33,14			
44,89				

Fig. 31

[8] Compare, for instance, S. P. Timoshenko, Elasticity Theory, Part I, 1934.

[9] In Fig. 41a the function values of u are given at one of the intermediate stages of the computation.

7

12,03	9,42	7,08	4,80	2,42
23,10	18,23	13,87	9,42	
32,37	26,10	20,12		
39,53	32,93			
44,80				

8

11,99	9,34	7,02	4,73	2,40
23,00	18,12	13,71	9,34	
32,30	25,91	19,98		
39,42	32,82			
44,76				

9

11,95	9,28	6,94	4,69	2,36
22,95	17,99	13,62	9,22	
32,20	25,80	19,81		
39,36	32,66			
44,71				

10

11,92	9,22	6,90	4,63	2,34
22,88	17,91	13,49	9,16	
32,14	25,66	19,71		
39,28	32,58			
44,68				

11

11,89	9,18	6,84	4,69	2,32
22,84	17,81	13,42	9,06	
32,07	25,58	19,58		
39,24	32,47			
44,64				

12

11,87	9,14	6,80	4,56	2,30
22,79	17,76	13,32	9,01	
32,03	25,48	19,50		
39,18	32,41			
44,62				

13

11,84	9,11	6,76	4,53	2,28
22,76	17,68	13,27	8,94	
31,98	25,42	19,40		
39,16	32,33			
44,59				

14

11,83	9,07	6,73	4,50	2,26
22,72	17,64	13,20	8,90	
31,95	25,35	19,34		
39,12	32,29			
44,58				

Fig. 31 (cont.)

15

11,81	9,05	6,69	4,47	2,25
22,70	17,58	13,15	8,85	
31,91	25,30	19,28		
39,10	32,24			
44,56				

16

11,80	9,02	6,67	4,45	2,24
22,67	17,55	13,10	8,81	
31,89	25,25	19,22		
39,07	32,20			
44,55				

17

11,78	9,00	6,64	4,43	2,22
22,66	17,51	13,06	8,78	
31,86	25,22	19,18		
39,05	32,16			
44,54				

18

11,78	8,98	6,62	4,41	2,22
22,64	17,48	13,03	8,74	
31,84	25,18	19,14		
39,03	32,14			
44,52				

19

11,77	8,97	6,60	4,40	2,20
22,62	17,46	13,00	8,72	
31,82	25,15	19,10		
39,02	32,10			
44,52				

20

11,76	8,96	6,59	4,38	2,20
22,61	17,44	12,97	8,70	
31,81	25,12	19,08		
39,00	32,08			
44,51				

21

11,76	8,95	6,58	4,37	2,19
22,60	17,42	12,95	8,68	
31,80	25,10	19,04		
38,99	32,06			
44,50				

22

11,75	8,94	6,57	4,36	2,18
22,59	17,40	12,93	8,66	
31,78	25,08	19,02		
38,98	32,04			
44,50				

Fig. 31 (cont.)

23

11,74	8,93	6,56	4,35	2,18
22,58	17,38	12,91	8,64	
31,78	25,06	19,00		
38,97	32,03			
44,49				

24

11,74	8,92	6,55	4,34	2,18
22,57	17,37	12,90	8,63	
31,76	25,05	18,98		
38,96	32,02			
44,48				

25

11,74	8,92	6,54	4,34	2,17
22,56	17,36	12,88	8,62	
31,76	25,03	18,98		
38,96	32,00			
44,48				

26

11,73	8,91	6,54	4,33	2,17
22,56	17,35	12,88	8,61	
31,75	25,02	18,96		
38,95	32,00			
44,48				

27

11,73	8,90	6,53	4,33	2,16
22,56	17,34	12,86	8,60	
31,74	25,02	18,95		
38,95	31,98			
44,48				

28

11,73	8,90	6,52	4,32	2,16
22,55	17,34	12,86	8,60	
31,74	25,00	18,94		
38,94	31,98			
44,48				

29

11,72	8,90	6,52	4,32	2,16
22,55	17,33	12,85	8,59	
31,74	25,00	18,93		
38,94	31,97			
44,47				

30

11,72	8,89	6,52	4,32	2,16
22,54	17,32	12,84	8,58	
31,74	24,99	18,92		
38,94	31,97			
44,47				

Fig. 31 (cont.)

31

11,72	8,89	6,51	4,32	2,16
22,54	17,32	12,84	8,58	
31,73	24,99	18,92		
38,94	31,95			
44,47				

32

11,72	8,89	6,51	4,31	2,16
22,54	17,32	12,83	8,58	
31,73	24,98	18,92		
38,93	31,96			
44,47				

33

11,72	8,89	6,51	4,31	2,16
22,54	17,31	12,83	8,57	
31,72	24,98	18,09		
38,93	31,96			
44,46				

34

11,72	8,88	6,51	4,31	2,16
22,54	17,31	12,82	8,57	
31,72	24,97	18,90		
38,92	31,96			
44,46				

35

11,72	8,88	6,50	4,31	2,16
22,54	17,30	12,82	8,56	
31,72	24,97	18,90		
38,92	31,94			
44,46				

36

11,72	8,88	6,50	4,30	2,16
22,53	17,30	12,82	8,56	
31,72	24,96	18,90		
38,92	31,94			
44,46				

37

11,72	8,88	6,50	4,30	2,15
22,53	17,30	12,82	8,56	
31,72	24,96	18,89		
38,92	31,94			
44,46				

38

11,72	8,88	6,50	4,30	2,15
22,53	17,30	12,81	8,56	
31,72	24,96	18,89		
38,92	31,94			
44,46				

Fig. 31 (cont.)

39

11,72	8,88	6,50	4,30	2,15
22,53	17,30	12,81	8,56	
31,72	24,96	18,88		
38,92	31,94			
44,46				

40

11,72	8,88	6,50	4,30	2,15
22,53	17,30	12,81	8,56	
31,72	24,96	18,88		
38,92	31,94			
44,46				

7—9

0,07	0,12	0,12	0,10	0,06
0,12	0,21	0,22	0,18	
0,16	0,25	0,27		
0,14	0,24			
0,08				

7—11

0,12	0,20	0,22	0,17	0,10
0,21	0,36	0,39	0,33	
0,27	0,43	0,48		
0,24	0,41			
0,14				

A

11,73	8,89	6,57	4,35	2,17
22,58	17,33	12,88	8,66	
31,70	24,97	18,96		
38,89	31,92			
44,46				

B

11,72	8,91	6,53	4,35	2,17
22,54	17,32	12,88	8,62	
31,71	24,98	18,93		
38,91	31,93			
44,45				

Fig. 31 (cont.)

Fig. 32

	0,00	0,00	0,00	0,00	0,00	
15,45	11,72	8,88	6,50	4,30	2,15	0,00
29,39	22,53	17,30	12,81	8,56	4,30	0,00
40,45	31,72	24,96	18,88	12,81	6,50	0,00
47,56	38,92	31,94	24,96	17,30	8,88	0,00
50,00	44,46	38,92	31,72	22,53	11,72	0,00
	50,00	47,56	40,45	29,39	15,45	

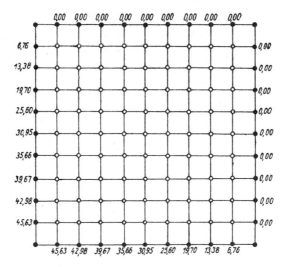

Fig. 33

	0,00	0,00	0,00	0,00	0,00	0,00	0,00	0,00	0,00	
6,76	5,86	5,06	4,34	3,68	3,04	2,42	1,82	1,21	0,60	
13,38	11,60	10,04	8,63	7,32	6,06	4,84	3,63	2,42		
19,70	17,12	14,86	12,81	10,89	9,04	7,23	5,43			
25,60	22,34	19,47	16,85	14,38	11,98	9,60				
30,95	27,17	23,82	20,73	17,78	14,88					
35,66	31,65	27,89	24,46	21,12						
39,67	35,50	31,72	28,09							
42,98	39,05	35,38								
45,63	42,34									

Fig. 34

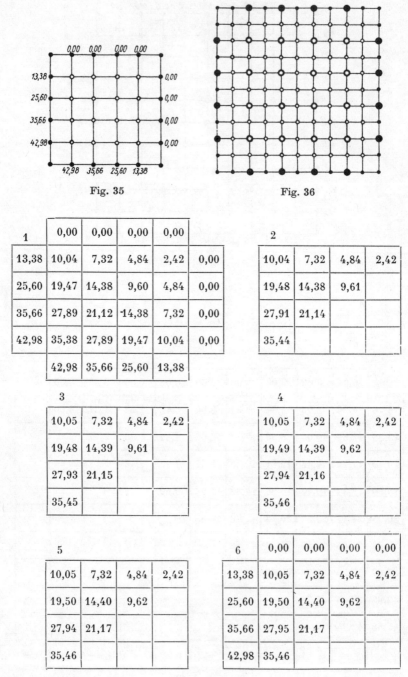

Fig. 35   Fig. 36

1

0,00	0,00	0,00	0,00	
13,38	10,04	7,32	4,84	2,42	0,00
25,60	19,47	14,38	9,60	4,84	0,00
35,66	27,89	21,12	14,38	7,32	0,00
42,98	35,38	27,89	19,47	10,04	0,00
	42,98	35,66	25,60	13,38	

2

10,04	7,32	4,84	2,42
19,48	14,38	9,61	
27,91	21,14		
35,44			

3

10,05	7,32	4,84	2,42
19,48	14,39	9,61	
27,93	21,15		
35,45			

4

10,05	7,32	4,84	2,42
19,49	14,39	9,62	
27,94	21,16		
35,46			

5

10,05	7,32	4,84	2,42
19,50	14,40	9,62	
27,94	21,17		
35,46			

6

	0,00	0,00	0,00	0,00
13,38	10,05	7,32	4,84	2,42
25,60	19,50	14,40	9,62	
35,66	27,95	21,17		
42,98	35,46			

Fig. 37

	0,00	0,00	0,00	0,00	0,00	0,00	0,00	0,00	0,00
6,76	5,86	5,06	4,34	3,68	3,04	2,42	1,82	1,21	0,60
13,38	11,60	10,04	8,63	7,32	6,06	4,84	3,63	2,42	
19,70	17,12	14,86	12,81	10,89	9,04	7,23	5,43		
25,60	22,34	19,47	16,85	14,38	11,98	9,60			
30,95	27,17	23,82	20,73	17,78	14,88				
35,66	31,56	27,89	24,46	21,12					
39,67	35,50	31,72	28,09						
42,98	39,05	35,38							
45,63	42,34								

Fig. 38

0,01	0,00	0,00	0,00
0,03	0,02	0,02	
0,06	0,05		
0,08			

Fig. 39

	0,003		0,000		0,000		0,000	
	0,010		0,007		0,007			
	0,020		0,017					
	0,027							

Fig. 40

At the center we have $\qquad\qquad u^{(1)} = 19{,}0;$

the first cycle gives the increment $\qquad \delta_1 = 0{,}2,$

the second $\qquad\qquad\qquad\qquad\qquad \delta_2 = 0{,}4.$

Instead of calculating with $\qquad\quad u^{(3)} = 19{,}0 + 0{,}2 + 0{,}4$

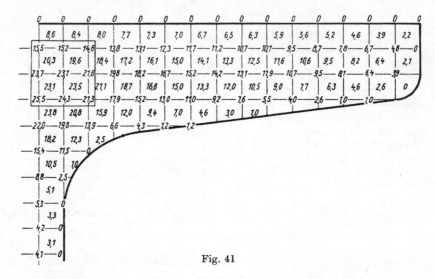

Fig. 41

we compute Orr's correction. By Formula 2 of Table 14, with the lateral dimensions assumed in the case in question for the rectangle on whose boundary the errors are practically equal to zero,

$$2m = 6, \qquad 2n = 5,$$

we find the following relation between the error ε and the difference δ after one cycle:

$$\varepsilon \approx 6(U' - U) = 6\delta.$$

As, by definition

$$u = U + \varepsilon$$

we obtain a better approximation in place of $u^{(3)}$, if we put

$$u^{(3)} = u^{(1)} + \delta_1 + \delta_2 + \varepsilon =$$
$$= u^{(1)} + \delta_1 + \delta_2 + 6\delta_2 =$$
$$= 19{,}0 + 0{,}2 + 0{,}4 + 6 \cdot 0{,}4 = 22{,}0.$$

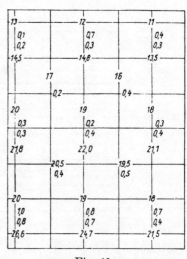

Fig. 41a

This value is also entered right at the center of Fig. 41a. It differs comparatively little from the final value 23.1 at this point that can be seen at the center of the lined-in square in main illustration 41.

Example 4 ([E17], p. 11). *Refinement of the Network.* Torsion of a keywayed shaft. As in the previous example, we are here dealing with the solution of the Poisson equation

$$\frac{\partial^2 u}{\partial x^2} + \frac{\partial^2 u}{\partial y^2} + 2 = 0$$

with vanishing boundary values. The solution is effected by the cross array, using Formula 2 of Table 11; $h = 1$ (shaft radius $= 10$).

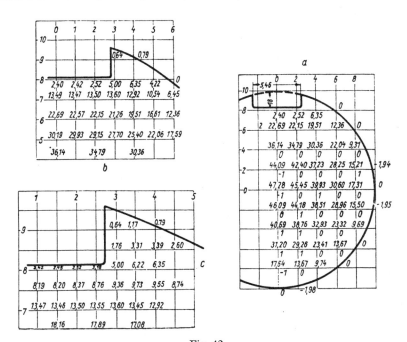

Fig. 42

The final solution is given in Fig. 42a. In order to get a more accurate idea of the change in function u at the reflex angle of the keyway slot, the results obtained by repeated refinement of the network are stated for $h = 0.5$ in Fig. 42b and for $h = 0.25$ in Fig. 42c.

Example 5 ([R37], p. 68). *Mikeladze's Improvement of Boundary Values.* The Dirichlet problem for an ellipse is to be solved for the equation

$$\frac{\partial^2 u}{\partial x^2} + \frac{\partial^2 u}{\partial y^2} = 6{,}25\, u + 40\, (x-1)\, e^{-2,5\, x}.$$

At the boundary of the ellipse $\qquad 4\, x^2 + 16\, y^2 = 1$

the required function u must equal zero. The solution is effected with a small number of points (32 points in the interior of the ellipse, see Fig. 43), and it is therefore essential to correct the boundary values as accurately as possible. The distribution of the *lattice points* in the ellipse is shown in Fig. 43; let the side of the square be $h = 0.1$. On grounds of symmetry, it is sufficient to look for u in half of the ellipse—hence in the lattice points 1—16. Hence, a *correction of the boundary values* must be effected at the points 1—7, 8, and 16, adjacent to the boundary points I—XI and forming the network field boundary. Since very few lattice points are taken, Mikeladze's more exact formulas will be used for this operation. The solution is carried out according to the following formulas:

a) *For the Interior Points 9—15.* As the given equation is of the form

$$\frac{\partial^2 u}{\partial x^2} + \frac{\partial^2 u}{\partial y^2} = g(x, y)\, u + f(x, y)$$

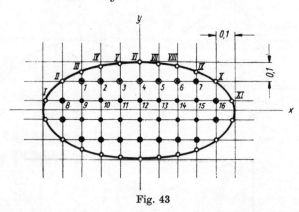

Fig. 43

when passing to difference according to Formulas 5 and 8 of Table 8, we obtain

$$\frac{u_{i+1,k} + u_{i-1,k} + u_{i,k+1} + u_{i,k-1} - 4u_{ik}}{h^2} = g_{ik}\, u_{ik} + f_{ik}$$

and hence $\qquad u_{ik} = \dfrac{u_{i+1,k} + u_{i-1,k} + u_{i,k+1} + u_{i,k-1}}{4 + h^2 g_{ik}} - \dfrac{h^2 f_{ik}}{4 + h^2 g_{ik}}.$

Thus at each interior point we have an equation of the form

$$u_0 = \frac{u_1 + u_2 + u_3 + u_4}{4 + h^2 g_0} - \frac{h^2 f_0}{4 + h^2 f_0}$$

if, as is customary, we denote with subscripts 1, 2, 3, and 4 the points adjacent to the point u_0.

In our case $\qquad\qquad\qquad g(x, y) = \text{constant},$
and actually at all points $\qquad\qquad g_0 = 6.25.$

Thus $\qquad\qquad\qquad 4 + h^2 g_0 = 4 + 0{,}1^2 \cdot 6{,}25 = 4{,}0625,$

and the equation finally appears as follows:

$$u_0 = \frac{u_1 + u_2 + u_3 + u_4}{4{,}0625} - \frac{0{,}01 f_0}{4{,}0625} = 0{,}24615 \, (u_1 + u_2 + u_3 + u_4) - 0{,}0024615 f_0.$$

Now for each point 9—15 there is, because of symmetry, an adjacent point of exactly the same function value. In our notation, this can be written

$$u_0 = u_1$$

and consequently: $u_0 = 0{,}32652 \, (u_2 + u_3 + u_4) - 0{,}0032652 \, f_0.$

b) *For the Boundary Points* 1—7, 8, *and* 16. We use Formula 1 of Table 13 for points 2—16, and Formula 3 of the same table for points 1—7, 8, and 16. For each of these points, the distances up to the nearest point on the boundary of the ellipse must be computed. Thus, for instance, for point 7 the distances up to points IX and X must be calculated. The coordinates of point IX are: $x = 0.30; y = 0.20$. For point X, we have $x = 0.40; y = 0.15$. Thus we get in Formula 3:

$$\delta = 0{,}05; \qquad \varepsilon = 0{,}10^{10}.$$

The value $f(x, y)$ at point 7 becomes

$$f_7 = 40 \, (0{,}3 - 1) \, e^{-2{,}5 \cdot 0{,}3} = - \, 13{,}227.$$

If all these values are substituted in formula 3, we find

$$u_7 = \frac{0{,}0075 \, u_6 + 0{,}02 \varphi_{IX} + 0{,}0075 \varphi_X + 0{,}01 u_{15}}{0{,}045469} - \frac{0{,}0005 \, (- \, 13{,}227)}{0{,}30312} =$$

$$= 0{,}16495 \, u_6 + 0{,}21993 \, u_{15} + 0{,}02182,$$

since $\qquad\qquad\qquad\qquad \varphi_{IX} = \varphi_X = 0.$

TABLE 15

1	2	3	4	5	6	7
0,58916	0,78655	0,76584	0,63631	0,46472	0,28962	0,13162
(0,59276)	(0,79139)	(0,77042)	(0,64000)	(0,46728)	(0,29113)	(0,13226)

8	9	10	11	12	13	14	15	16
0,86783	1,26332	1,31118	1,17433	0,95448	0,71255	0,48271	0,28206	0,11722
(0,86985)	(1,27020)	(1,31898)	(1,18131)	(0,96000)	(0,71650)	(0,48522)	(0,28342)	(0,11772)

---

[10] It must be borne in mind that when $\epsilon = h$, Formula 3 of Table 13 turns into Formula 1, as must naturally be the case, substituting the boundary value φ_3 for the value u_i in Formula 1.

In this way, we obtain the following set of equations:

$$u_1 = 0,21993\,u_9 + 0,16495\,u_2 + 0,18158;$$
$$u_2 = 0,24325\,u_{10} + 0,21786\,(u_1 + u_3) + 0,17241;$$
$$u_3 = 0,24609\,u_{11} + 0,23988\,(u_2 + u_4) + 0,13553;$$
$$u_4 = 0,24615\,(u_3 + u_5 + u_{12}) + 0,09846;$$
$$u_5 = 0,24609\,u_{13} + 0,23988\,(u_4 + u_6) + 0,06726;$$
$$u_6 = 0,24325\,u_{14} + 0,21786\,(u_5 + u_7) + 0,04228;$$
$$u_7 = 0,21993\,u_{15} + 0,16495\,u_6 + 0,02182;$$
$$u_8 = 0,32039\,u_9 + 0,46307;$$
$$u_9 = 0,32652\,(u_1 + u_8 + u_{10}) + 0,35946;$$
$$u_{10} = 0,32652\,(u_2 + u_9 + u_{11}) + 0,25841;$$
$$u_{11} = 0,32652\,(u_3 + u_{10} + u_{12}) + 0,18448;$$
$$u_{12} = 0,32652\,(u_4 + u_{11} + u_{13}) + 0,13061;$$
$$u_{13} = 0,32652\,(u_5 + u_{12} + u_{14}) + 0,09154;$$
$$u_{14} = 0,32652\,(u_6 + u_{13} + u_{15}) + 0,06338;$$
$$u_{15} = 0,32652\,(u_7 + u_{14} + u_{16}) + 0,04319;$$
$$u_{16} = 0,32039\,u_{15} + 0,02685.$$

When the set, as usual, is solved by the iteration method, we get the values exhibited in Table 15. For comparison, the correct values are shown in parentheses in the same boxes.

3. *The Neumann Problem and the Third Boundary Value Problem*

The Neumann Problem. In the Neumann problem, the values given at the boundary of domain G are not those of the function itself but of the derivatives of its normals:

$$\frac{\partial u}{\partial n} = \frac{\partial u}{\partial x}\cos\alpha + \frac{\partial u}{\partial y}\sin\alpha.$$

Here α is the angle made with the x-axis by the normal at the field boundary. For the problem to have a unique solution, we must have

$$\int_c \frac{\partial u}{\partial n}\,ds = 0 \tag{7}$$

and, moreover, the function value must be given at some boundary point or at a point in the interior of the domain.

For the approximate solution of this problem, we make a transition to the network (for fuller details hereon see below), just as in the case of the Dirichlet problem, and assume that at the boundary of the network domain $\bar{G}$, the difference of the normals

$$u_\nu = u_0 - u_1 \tag{8}$$

is given; let the value of u at the boundary be denoted in this case by u_0 and the value at the point in the interior of the domain nearest to the boundary point under consideration by u_1 (Fig. 44).

The condition (7) is replaced by the following:

$$\sum u_\nu = 0,$$

where the summation may be extended over the whole boundary of the domain $\bar{G}$. The values of the difference of the normals on transition from domain G to domain $\bar{G}$ are determined, just as are the values of the function itself in the case of the Dirichlet problem, by the formula

$$u_\nu = h \frac{\partial u}{\partial n}$$

for instance, by extrapolation (interpolation) from the given values u on the boundary of G. Here the magnitude of a side of the square network is denoted by n in exactly the same units as $\frac{\partial u}{\partial n}$ was computed. The derivative is computed in direction toward the *exterior* normal.

Fig. 44

We now show how the Neumann problem reduces to the Dirichlet problem on approximate solution. We assume as first approximation any arbitrarily selected values $u_0^{(1)}$ of function u on the boundary of $\bar{G}$. For these values we solve the Dirichlet problem. After having found the solution, we know the values of the function u at all interior points of the domain and can find u_ν by formula (8). These values u_ν are, of course, different from the given values. In order to smooth this difference, we change the values on the boundary by putting

$$u_0^{(2)} = u_\nu + u_1^{(1)}$$

Here u_ν is the given difference of the normals and $u_1^{(1)}$ the value of the function $u^{(1)}$, determined by means of the boundary values $u_0^{(1)}$ at the adjacent points of the boundary. For these new boundary values $u_0^{(2)}$ we again solve the Dirichlet problem and find fresh values $u_1^{(2)}$ of the function $u^{(2)}$ at the points lying nearest the boundary. Then we put

$$u_0^{(3)} = u_\nu + u_1^{(2)} \qquad\qquad \text{and so on.}$$

The general formula reads:

$$u_0^{(n+1)} = u_\nu + u_1^{(n)} \tag{9}$$

The sequence will converge and determine the function u, which serves as solution of the Neumann problem. In order to obtain the definite solution, we still have to see how far the values found for u at each point at which the function value itself was given from the beginning, differs from such value, and add this difference to all the values found. Accordingly, the solution of the Neumann problem is reduced to the solution of a series of Dirichlet problems.

In practice it would, of course, not be feasible to carry out the numerical computation in such a way that for every fresh $u_0^{(n)}$ at the boundary, the Dirichlet problem could be carried through to the end. The procedure is as follows: When the consecutive systems of arithmetic means for the solution of the Dirichlet problem are computed, *the boundary values must also be simultaneously refined* in accordance with formula (9). In this method the solution of the Dirichlet problem and the refinement of the boundary values will thus be simultaneously pushed ahead, effecting a great saving in calculation.

Transition to the Network Domain. In the case of the Neumann problem or the third boundary problem, the question of transition from the given boundary of the domain to the network boundary becomes very involved, because derivatives in the direction of the normals appear in the boundary conditions. In this transition the derivative of the normal must be replaced by differences in the direction of the network lines. The general formula ([R31], p. 192), by means of which this substitution is effected, is as follows:

$$\frac{\partial u}{\partial n} \approx \frac{1}{\sin (\alpha + \beta)} \left[\frac{u_0 - u_1}{l_1} \sin \alpha + \frac{u_0 - u_2}{l_2} \sin \beta \right]. \tag{10}$$

Here α and β are the angles made by the normals with two directions through network points (see Fig. 45), u_0, u_1, u_2 the function values at those points that are indicated by the figures 0, 1, 2 (where 0 lies on the boundary), l_1 and l_2 the distance of the points 1 and 2 from point 0; the derivative is taken in the direction of the exterior normal.[11]

In the most frequently occurring particular cases, Formula 10 assumes a simpler form, as shown in Table 16.

It must of course be noted that up to the present the question of transition from the boundary conditions of the given domain to those of the network in each case, when the normal derivative enters into these conditions, has been extremely badly worked out. In all problems of this type hitherto solved, the given boundary simply coincides with the network boundary so that there is no need for the transition.

Computation array. For the numerical solution of the Neumann problem a traverse must be prepared just as in the case of the Dirichlet problem, but now no longer in accordance with Fig. 21c, since not only the interior but also the boundary values are to be improved. The first traverse has the form shown in Fig. 46. The outermost row of the network is intended for recording the given differences of the normals. The arrows show to which boundary point each difference belongs. As for the rest, the computations proceed in exactly the same sequence as when solving the Dirichlet problem; we need not, therefore, discuss this question in further detail.

---

[11] In [R31] the derivative of the interior normal is taken. This explains the difference in sign between our formulas and those of that particular textbook.

TABLE 16

Formulas for Substitution of Derivatives of the Normals by Differences

No.	Net	Pattern	Formula
1	square		$\dfrac{\partial u}{\partial n} \approx \dfrac{u_0 - u_1}{h}$
2	square		$\dfrac{\partial u}{\partial n} \approx \dfrac{\sqrt{2}}{2}\left[\dfrac{u_0 - u_1}{h} + \dfrac{u_0 - u_2}{h}\right]$
3	square		$\dfrac{\partial u}{\partial n} \approx \dfrac{u_0 - u_1}{h}\sin\alpha + \dfrac{u_0 - u_2}{h}\cos\alpha$
4	rectangular		$\dfrac{\partial u}{\partial n} \approx \dfrac{u_0 - u_1}{h}\sin\alpha + \dfrac{u_0 - u_2}{k}\cos\alpha$
5	equilateral triangle		$\dfrac{\partial u}{\partial n} \approx \dfrac{2\sqrt{3}}{3}\left[\dfrac{u_0 - u_1}{h}\sin\alpha + \dfrac{u_0 - u_2}{h}\sin\left(\dfrac{\pi}{3} - \alpha\right)\right]$

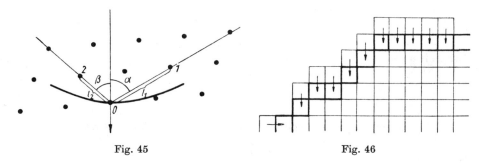

Fig. 45   Fig. 46

Third Boundary Value Problem. In the third boundary value problem we have the following boundary condition for the function u:

$$au + b\,\frac{\partial u}{\partial n} = c. \tag{11}$$

Here a, b, c are known functions defined for each boundary point of domain G, inside which the function u is sought, and $\dfrac{\partial u}{\partial n}$ denotes the derivative of this function toward the exterior normals on the boundary of G. So that the problem shall have a unique solution, we assume that the functions a and b have one and the same sign at all boundary points, and that they do not vanish simultaneously.

For the approximate solution of this problem, we again have recourse to a network domain $\bar{G}$, while substituting the boundary conditions (11) as follows:

$$a u_0 + b\, \frac{u_\nu}{h} = c. \tag{12}$$

Here u_ν is the normal difference

$$u_\nu = u_0 - u_1$$

and h, as usual, denotes the side of the network square.

If we denote the magnitude $\dfrac{b}{h}$ by $\varkappa$, then we can write (12) in the form

$$a u_0 + \varkappa u_\nu = c$$

or

$$a u_0 + \varkappa (u_0 - u_1) = c$$

or, finally,

$$u_0 = \frac{c + \varkappa u_1}{a + \varkappa}. \tag{13}$$

This relation must be satisfied on the boundary of domain $\bar{G}$. The solution itself is completely analogous to the solution of the Neumann problem, with the one difference that when solving the Neumann problem, we determined the new boundary values from the relation

$$u_0^{(n+1)} = u_\nu + u_1^{(n)}$$

(where u_ν denotes the given values of the difference of the normals), while we now determine them from the formula

$$u_0^{(n+1)} = \frac{c + \varkappa u_1^{(n)}}{a + \varkappa}$$

which is a consequence of (13).[12]

Examples for the Solution of the Neumann and Third Boundary Value Problems

Example 1 ([G61], p. 136). *Solution of the Neumann Problem for a Square.* In Fig. 47,0 the differences of the normals toward the *interior* normal are given; in the top left corner of the traverse the value of the required function for $u = 50$ is given.

---

[12] The computation array is exactly the same as for the Neumann problem.

The solution is performed without any device that could improve the convergence, in accordance with Formula 1 of Table 9. The boundary values are improved only after the Dirichlet problem for the actual starting values is solved to the end.

Fig. 47,1 gives the initial distribution of the values (function $u^{(1)}$), in Fig. 47,2 the boundary values are improved in such manner that the necessary differences of the normals are obtained, and the Dirichlet problem is solved according to these values

0	10	11	12	15	20	
20	50					— 2
50						—15
40						—30
20						—20
6						—10
	—30	—45	—30	—5	3	a

Fig. 47

1

	40	45	50	55	60	
30	43	57	69	81	92	100
20	47	69	88	107	128	150
10	55	85	108	130	161	220
40	78	108	127	143	165	200
60	107	141	149	150	156	170
	150	200	180	150	140	$u^{(1)}$

2

	33	46	57	66	72	
23	40	56	71	84	93	94
17	46	69	88	105	122	143
15	58	86	106	125	149	191
58	85	109	126	140	159	185
101	116	140	149	150	157	166
	137	186	179	155	153	$u^{(2)}$

Fig. 47 (cont.)

3

	30	45	59	69	73	
20	38	56	72	84	93	95
16	46	69	87	103	119	137
18	60	86	105	123	144	139
65	90	111	126	138	154	178
110	122	142	149	150	156	167
	145	195	179	155	154	$u^{(3)}$

4

	28	45	63	69	73	
18	37	56	72	84	93	95
16	46	69	87	103	118	134
20	61	87	106	122	142	174
70	92	112	126	137	152	174
116	126	144	149	149	155	166
	192	187	179	155	153	$u^{(4)}$

5

	26	44	58	67	70	
16	36	55	70	82	90	92
16	46	69	86	101	115	130
24	64	88	105	120	138	168
78	98	116	127	136	149	169
129	135	149	151	148	152	162
	165	194	181	153	149	$u^{(13)}$

6

	40	58	72	81	84	
30	50	69	84	96	104	106
30	60	83	100	115	129	144
38	78	102	119	134	152	182
92	112	130	141	150	163	183
143	149	163	165	162	166	176
	179	208	195	167	163	$u^{(13)}+14$

Fig. 47 (cont.)

(function $u^{(2)}$ was found). The remaining traverses show the further course of the computation. Traverse 47,5, which is marked $u^{(13)}$ (thirteenth approximation), already has differences of the normals equal to those given, the discrepancy in u still amounts to 14 units (the difference 50—36 in the top corner equals 14).

The final value of function u is given by the last traverse 47,6 for $u = u^{(13)} + 14$.

Example 2. Solution of the Third Boundary Value Problem for a Rectangle. Consider the distribution of heat in an insulated wall with one part free from insulation; temperature is kept constant in one part, while in another part a free exchange of heat takes place (Fig. 48).

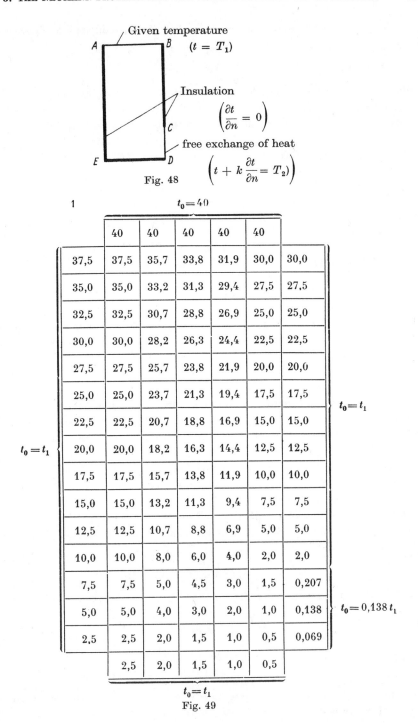

Fig. 48

Fig. 49

The problem is reduced to the solution of the Laplace differential equation

$$\frac{\partial^2 t}{\partial x^2} + \frac{\partial^2 t}{\partial y^2} = 0$$

for the interior of the rectangle $ABCDE$ with the following boundary conditions which are already expressed in differences:

$$t = 40 \qquad \text{in the boundary portion } AB$$
$$t_\nu = 0 \qquad \text{in the parts } BC \text{ and } AED$$
$$20.0 t_0 + 3.2 t_\nu = 0 \qquad \text{in the part } CD.$$

t_ν denotes the difference of the normals

$$t_\nu = t_0 - t_1$$

where t_0 is the value at the boundary and t_1 that at the nearest interior point. The mixed boundary condition on CD can also be written thus

$$t_0 = 0,138 t_1 \tag{14}$$

and on BC and AED $\qquad t_0 = t_1.$

The solution is effected with simultaneous refinement of the boundary values in accordance with Formula 1 of Table 11. Fig. 49,1 gives the initial distribution, and plates 49,2—9 show the first traverses, obtained through a simple computation of the arithmetic means. The boundary values are omitted, beyond those in that part of the boundary where they were computed in accordance with Formula (14). Fig. 49,10 shows the final solution, which in the case in question required approximately 70 traverses (the solution was effected without any refinement of the convergence). Fig. 50 represents the actual distribution of temperature, and Fig. 51 shows the isothermal chart.

Example 3 ([G56], p. 187). We will consider the solution of the following problem in greater detail.

Determine the **thermal condition at the corner of a brick wall,** one and a half bricks thick, when the temperature inside the house is constant at $t_i = 40°\text{C}$ and the external air temperature is constant at $t_a = 0°$.[13]

If the temperature of the interior wall surface be denoted by t_i' and of the outer one by t_a', then for the flow of heat through the interior surface we have the well-known expression

$$Q_0 = \lambda \frac{\partial t}{\partial n} = \alpha_1 (t_i - t_i')$$

and for the flow through the outer surface

$$Q_0 = - \lambda \frac{\partial t}{\partial n} = \alpha_2 (t_a' - t_a).[14]$$

In our case $\lambda = 0.6$; $\alpha_1 = 7.5$; $\alpha_2 = 20.0$.

---

[13] The solution clearly holds for arbitrary values t_i and t_a at $t_i - t_a = 40°\text{C}$, since the corresponding distributions of temperature differ from each other by a constant magnitude only.

[14] The derivatives are taken in the sense of the exterior normals.

2

37,05	36,12	34,72	33,30	32,35	
34,55	33,18	31,30	29,40	27,98	
32,05	30,68	28,80	26,90	25,48	
29,55	28,18	26,30	24,40	22,98	
27,05	25,68	23,80	21,90	20,48	
24,55	23,18	21,30	19,40	17,98	
22,05	20,68	18,80	16,20	15,48	
19,55	18,18	16,30	14,40	12,98	
17,05	15,68	13,80	11,90	10,48	
14,55	13,18	11,30	9,40	7,98	
12,05	10,62	8,78	6,80	5,35	
9,50	7,92	6,32	4,45	3,12	
6,38	6,00	4,25	3,00	1,55	0,214
4,75	3,75	3,00	2,00	1,03	0,142
3,00	2,25	1,88	1,25	0,64	0,088

3

36,93	36,24	35,18	34,14	33,41	
34,21	33,16	31,52	29,87	28,80	
31,71	30,55	20,80	27,02	25,84	
29,21	28,05	26,30	24,52	23,34	
26,71	25,58	23,80	22,02	20,84	
24,21	23,05	21,30	19,52	18,34	
21,71	20,55	18,80	17,02	15,84	
19,21	18,05	16,30	14,52	13,34	
16,71	15,55	13,80	12,02	10,84	
14,21	13,04	11,29	9,50	8,30	
11,68	10,48	8,76	7,00	5,71	
8,96	8,11	6,35	4,81	3,62	
6,66	5,58	4,58	3,06	1,84	0,254
4,47	4,00	2,97	2,07	1,08	0,149
3,25	2,72	2,03	1,44	0,75	0,103

4

36,84	36,32	35,48	34,62	34,09	
34,00	33,13	31,75	30,37	29,48	
31,42	30,43	28,85	27,26	26,25	
28,92	28,63	26,29	24,67	23,93	
26,42	25,40	23,79	22,17	21,14	
23,92	22,90	21,29	19,67	18,64	
21,42	20,40	18,79	17,17	16,14	
18,92	17,90	16,29	14,67	13,64	
16,42	15,40	13,79	12,16	11,12	
13,91	12,88	11,28	9,45	7,94	
11,33	10,40	8,78	6,94	6,16	
8,85	7,87	6,56	5,01	4,00	
6,42	5,84	4,49	3,32	2,00	0,276
4,60	3,94	3,17	2,14	1,20	0,166
3,42	3,00	2,24	1,57	0,84	0,116

5

36,79	36,36	35,67	34,98	34,55	
33,85	33,12	31,96	30,76	30,05	
31,19	30,51	28,93	27,54	26,74	
28,85	27,76	26,48	24,91	24,00	
26,16	25,44	23,79	22,32	21,74	
23,66	22,75	21,29	19,82	18,90	
21,16	20,25	18,79	17,32	16,40	
18,66	17,75	16,29	14,82	13,74	
16,16	15,25	13,78	12,28	11,22	
13,64	12,75	11,22	9,58	8,67	
11,12	10,22	8,80	7,35	6,26	
8,62	7,91	6,54	5,20	4,29	
6,43	5,68	4,72	3,14	2,20	0,304
4,60	4,15	3,20	2,06	1,29	0,178
3,61	3,15	2,50	1,70	0,93	0,128

Fig. 49 (cont.)

6

36,75	36,40	35,82	35,24	34,90	
33,74	33,17	32,12	31,13	30,52	
31,10	30,25	29,12	27,84	27,08	
28,49	27,82	27,04	25,08	24,28	
26,03	25,12	23,88	22,50	21,67	
23,43	22,66	21,29	19,96	19,15	
20,93	20,11	18,79	17,46	16,59	
18,43	17,61	16,28	14,90	14,04	
15,93	15,11	13,80	12,35	11,47	
13,42	12,58	11,23	9,88	8,93	
10,90	10,14	8,83	7,46	6,64	
8,52	7,76	6,66	5,40	4,49	
6,33	5,80	4,71	3,54	2,32	0,320
4,70	4,16	3,36	2,40	1,34	0,185
3,74	3,35	2,64	1,80	1,01	0,139

7

36,72	36,44	35,94	35,46	35,14	
33,69	33,13	32,31	31,43	30,91	
30,88	30,30	29,31	28,13	27,43	
28,36	27,72	26,50	25,42	24,55	
25,77	25,10	23,99	22,67	21,90	
23,26	22,49	21,32	20,10	19,34	
20,72	20,00	18,79	17,55	16,81	
18,22	17,48	16,28	15,03	14,25	
15,72	14,98	13,74	12,46	11,67	
13,21	12,48	11,27	9,99	9,23	
10,74	10,00	8,87	7,64	6,88	
8,38	7,78	6,68	5,54	4,71	
6,34	5,74	4,84	3,74	2,42	0,334
4,73	4,30	3,48	2,51	1,48	0,204
3,88	3,47	2,79	1,06	1,07	0,148

8

36,71	36,45	36,05	35,64	35,38	
33,60	33,18	32,45	31,70	31,23	
30,81	30,26	29,31	28,40	27,80	
28,20	27,56	26,61	25,46	24,82	
25,62	24,99	23,90	22,85	22,12	
23,06	22,42	21,34	20,22	19,54	
20,62	19,87	18,79	17,68	16,99	
18,04	17,37	16,26	15,24	14,44	
15,41	14,86	13,75	12,61	11,90	
13,04	12,36	11,27	10,15	9,44	
10,58	9,97	8,90	7,82	7,12	
8,34	7,70	6,76	5,68	4,89	
6,30	5,82	4,91	3,84	2,56	0,353
4,81	4,36	3,61	2,66	1,55	0,214
3,99	3,61	2,92	2,08	1,16	0,160

9

36,69	36,48	36,14	35,78	35,56	
33,58	33,19	32,56	31,93	31,55	
30,72	30,22	29,43	28,57	28,06	
28,05	27,52	26,56	25,67	25,05	
25,47	24,88	23,95	22,93	22,33	
22,93	22,32	21,33	20,35	19,72	
20,40	19,80	18,79	17,81	17,16	
17,86	17,21	16,29	15,25	14,64	
15,34	14,72	13,75	12,76	12,10	
12,82	12,28	11,29	10,28	9,65	
10,48	9,88	8,96	7,96	7,32	
8,23	7,70	6,80	5,83	5,06	
6,32	5,82	5,01	3,95	2,66	0,367
4,86	4,46	3,71	2,77	1,65	0,228
4,10	3,72	3,06	2,20	1,24	0,171

Fig. 49 (cont.)

10						
	40	40	40	40	40	
36,9	36,9	36,9	36,9	36,9	36,9	36,9
33,8	33,8	33,8	33,8	33,8	33,8	33,8
30,8	30,8	30,8	30,8	30,8	30,8	30,8
27,8	27,8	27,8	27,8	27,8	27,8	27,8
25,0	25,0	25,0	25,0	25,0	25,0	25,0
22,2	22,2	22,2	22,2	22,2	22,2	22,2
19,6	19,6	19,6	19,6	19,6	19,6	19,6
17,2	17,2	17,2	17,2	17,2	17,2	17,2
15,0	15,0	15,0	15,0	14,9	14,8	14,8
13,0	13,0	13,0	12,8	12,6	12,5	12,5
11,1	11,1	11,0	10,8	10,4	10,1	10,1
9,4	9,4	9,2	8,8	8,2	7,5	7,5
8,1	8,1	7,8	7,2	6,1	4,3	0,59
7,2	7,2	6,8	6,0	4,8	3,0	0,41
6,6	6,6	6,2	5,4	4,2	2,5	0,34
	6,6	6,2	5,4	4,2	2,5	

Fig. 49 (cont.)

We obtain the boundary conditions:

$$0{,}6 \, \frac{\partial t}{\partial n} = 7{,}5 \, (40{,}0 - t)$$

on the inside surface, and

$$- \, 0{,}6 \, \frac{\partial t}{\partial n} = 20{,}0 \, t$$

on the outside. In the interior of the wall, as is well known:

$$\frac{\partial^2 t}{\partial x^2} + \frac{\partial^2 t}{\partial y^2} = 0.$$

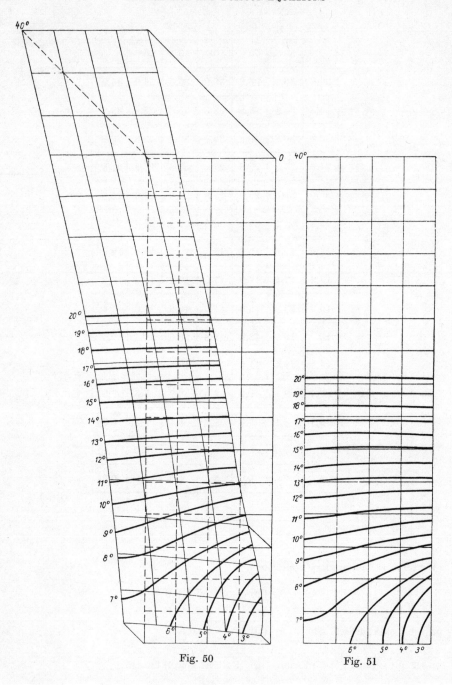

Fig. 50

Fig. 51

We consequently reach the boundary value problem, *to determine the harmonic function t in the interior of the domain S (Fig. 52), with the boundary conditions;*

$$7{,}5\,t + 0{,}6\frac{\partial t}{\partial n} = 300{,}0 \tag{15}$$

on the part ABC of the boundary and $20{,}0\,t + 0{,}6\,\frac{\partial t}{\partial n} = 0 \tag{16}$

on the part DEF.

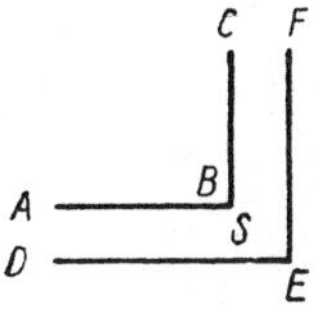

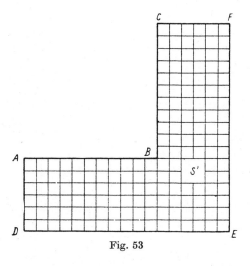

Fig. 52

For computation purposes we split up the interior of domain S into squares (in our example 6 rows of squares are taken) and transform the boundary conditions by writing them in the form of differences. Clearly

$$t_{\nu} = t_0 - t_1 \approx \frac{l}{6}\frac{\partial t}{\partial n}.$$

Here l is the thickness of the wall in meters; t_0 the temperature at the boundary, t_1 the temperature at the closest internal point. In our case $l = .375$ m. and consequently

$$t_{\nu} = 0{,}0625\,\frac{\partial t}{\partial n}$$

or $$\frac{\partial t}{\partial n} = 16 t_{\nu}.$$

Thus the boundary conditions (15) and (16) become

$$7{,}5\,t_0 + 9{,}6\,t_{\nu} = 300{,}0 \tag{17}$$

on ABC, and

$$20{,}0\,t_0 + 9{,}6\,t_{\nu} = 0 \tag{18}$$

on DEF.

Fig. 53

1

33,40	33,40	33,40	33,40	33,40	33,40	33,40	33,40	33,40	33,40	33,40					
28,25	28,25	28,25	28,20	28,15	28,10	28,00	27,90	27,55	26,85	25,25	21,15				
23,10	23,10	23,05	23,00	22,90	22,80	22,70	22,50	22,00	21,10	19,60	17,00	14,00			
17,95	17,95	19,90	17,80	17,70	17,60	17,45	17,25	16,80	16,05	14,85	13,15	11,15	9,00		
12,80	12,75	12,70	12,65	12,60	12,50	12,40	12,20	11,90	11,35	10,55	9,50	8,20	6,85	5,40	
7,65	7,65	7,65	7,65	7,60	7,55	7,50	7,35	7,14	6,85	6,45	5,95	5,35	4,70	3,95	3,25
2,47	2,47	2,47	2,47	2,47	2,47	2,47	2,47	2,47	2,47	2,47	2,47	2,47	2,47	2,47	2,47

Fig. 54

2

33,40	33,39	33,38	33,34	33,26	33,17	33,01	32,75	32,33	31,67	30,50					
28,25	28,24	28,20	28,12	28,00	27,84	27,55	27,10	26,35	25,17	23,10	19,06				
23,10	23,08	23,03	22,93	22,80	22,60	22,20	21,67	20,82	19,57	17,71	15,04	12,12			
17,95	17,93	17,88	17,78	17,62	17,40	17,05	16,50	15,72	14,65	13,20	11,32	9,24	7,11		
12,80	12,78	12,73	12,65	12,50	12,30	12,01	11,57	10,96	10,16	9,13	7,86	6,47	5,01	3,55	
7,65	7,63	7,60	7,54	7,45	7,30	7,10	6,83	6,45	5,96	5,35	4,63	3,82	2,97	2,11	1,25
2,47	2,47	2,46	2,44	2,42	2,36	2,30	2,22	2,09	1,93	1,73	1,50	1,24	0,96	0,68	0,40

Fig. 54 (cont.)

The domain S is boundless. Hence we change the problem slightly by making use of the fact that at some distance from the corner, the temperature distribution must be practically much the same as in an unbounded plane wall; sectioning the wall at a sufficient distance from the corner (11 squares away from B in our example, see Fig. 53), for boundary values on the sides AD and CF we assume the temperature distribution that would occur in the case of an endless wall. We utilize the same distribution also as a first approximation in the remaining network points.

The thermal state of an infinite wall is, of course, clearly determinable from elementary principles.[15]

If we complete the necessary calculations, we obtain the following values for the temperature at the inner and outer surfaces of the endless wall:

$$T_i = 33.40, \qquad T_a = 2.47.$$

We now proceed to the solution of the main problem. The boundary conditions (17) and (18) give the computation formulae in the form:

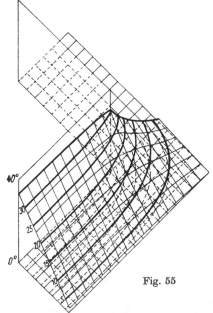

$$t_0^{(n+1)} = 17{,}55 + 0{,}561\, t_1^{(n)}$$

on the part ABC of the boundary,

$$t_0^{(n+1)} = 0{,}324\, t_1^{(n)}$$

on the boundary portion DEF.

Fig. 55

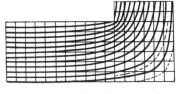

Fig. 56

As a first approximation we put: $t_0 = 33.4$ on ABC and $t_1 = 2.47$ on DEF; on the sides AD and CF we assume the boundary values according to a linear gradient between T_i and T_a, and retain these unchanged during the whole course of the computation.

---

[15] In this case, if we consider a cross section of the wall, we have inside, instead of the Laplace equation, simply

$$\frac{\partial^2 t}{\partial x^2} = 0, \quad \text{and hence } t = c_1 x + c_2,$$

and the problem is reduced to the determination of the constants c_1 and c_2 from the boundary conditions (15) and (16), i.e. to the solution of a system of two linear equations.

In Fig. 54,1 the initial approximation is shown (on account of symmetry only half the network domain is reproduced). Fig. 54,2 gives the final result.

To expedite calculation, the first approximations were carried out with less precision than the final ones. (Discrepancies up to 5 units in the last decimal place in the earlier approximations and of 1 to 2 units in the later ones).

Fig. 55 shows temperature distribution obtained. Fig. 56 gives the isotherms.

4. *Solution of the Laplace Equation by Use of a Mapping of the Region*

General Introduction. The Dirichlet problem may be solved for a domain G (Fig. 57a), if the conformal mapping of this domain in some other simpler domain G_1 (e.g. the rectangle in Fig. 57b) is known. The mapping is achieved by means of the function of a complex variable

$$\zeta = \varphi(z);$$

where $\qquad\qquad \zeta = \xi + i\eta, \qquad\qquad z = x + iy.$

Furthermore, let $\qquad\quad \varphi(z) = f(x, y) + i g(x, y).$

Then the map is given by the functions

$$\xi = f(x, y),$$
$$\eta = g(x, y)$$

in which it is known that the equation

$$\frac{\partial^2 u}{\partial x^2} + \frac{\partial^2 u}{\partial y^2} = 0$$

transforms into $\qquad\qquad \dfrac{\partial^2 u}{\partial \xi^2} + \dfrac{\partial^2 u}{\partial \eta^2} = 0 \qquad\qquad$ in this projection.

If we effect the transition of the boundary values of the function u from the boundary of domain G to the boundary of domain G_1 in such a way that identical boundary values obtain in the corresponding points of both boundaries, then by solving the Dirichlet problem for domain G_1 we have also solved the Dirichlet problem for domain G, since the values of function u in the conformal projection of domain G on G_1 remain the same at corresponding points (e.g., a and a_1). For domain G_1, however, the Dirichlet problem is easier to solve, and hence in such cases, where the conformal projection of a given domain on some other simpler one is known, this can be utilized in order to facilitate the solution.

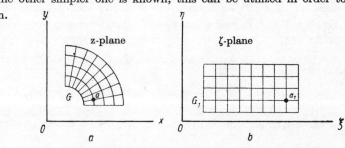

Fig. 57

Example ([E17], p. 17). Solve the *torsion problem for a hollow shaft with milled longitudinal slots* (as, for instance, at the end of aircraft engine driving shafts on which the airscrew bushes are mounted). The outer diameter of the shaft is equal to 10 inches, the number of slots is 30; the cross section of the shaft is shown in Fig. 58.

Solution of the torsion problem is equivalent to solving the equation

$$\frac{\partial^2 u}{\partial x^2} + \frac{\partial^2 u}{\partial y^2} = 0$$

with the boundary conditions $u = \frac{1}{2}(x^2 + y^2) + c_1.$ (19)

For reasons of symmetry, we will solve the problem only for the portion of the shaft shown in Fig. 59.

Using the function $\zeta = m \ln z$

the curvilinear quadrilateral $ABCD$ (Fig. 59) is transformed into a rectangle. In this case

$$\xi = m \ln r,$$
$$\eta = m\Theta,$$

when $z = re^{i\theta}.$

The factor m is so chosen that the transformed domain (rectangle $A'B'C'D'$, Fig. 60) takes dimensions convenient for the computation.

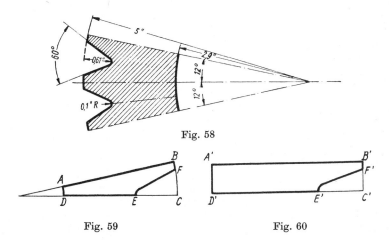

Fig. 58

Fig. 59   Fig. 60

In the case in question it is expedient to choose m so that the height $A'D'$ of the rectangle contains an integral number of units and that the sides of the rectangle consequently fit into a network system. The portion of the boundary of the transformed domain $B'F'E'$, corresponding to the profile of the milled slot BFE is approximately mapped by adhering to the isogonality and similitude of small elements corresponding to each other in both domains.

The boundary values on the outer portion of the boundary BFE (Fig. 59) are determined by formula (19) and transferred into the corresponding points of the transformed boundary $B'F'E'$ (Fig. 60); the boundary values on the inner portion AD of the boundary should be constant.

From the general principles of torsion theory, it follows in fact that the function

$$\psi = u - \frac{1}{2}\,(x^2 + y^2)$$

must be constant for each boundary of a multiply connected domain for which the torsion problem is solved. As

$$x^2 + y^2 = \text{const},$$

on the circle of which arc AD is a part,

$$u = C \tag{20}$$

must hold on this arc. The magnitude of the constants C is determined from the condition

$$\int_L \frac{\partial u}{\partial n}\,ds = 0 \tag{21}$$

where the integral is extended over the inner boundary. For reasons of symmetry, it follows from this, that

$$\int_{AD} \frac{\partial u}{\partial n}\,ds = 0$$

Now
$$\int_{AD} \frac{\partial u}{\partial n}\,ds = - \int_0^{\frac{\pi}{30}} \frac{\partial u}{\partial r}\,r\,d\theta = - \int_{A'D'} \frac{\partial u}{\partial \xi}\,\frac{m}{r}\,r\,\frac{1}{m}\,d\eta = - \int_{A'D'} \frac{\partial u}{\partial \xi}\,d\eta.$$

Consequently, as it relates to our problem, the condition (21) gives

$$\int \frac{\partial u}{\partial \xi}\,d\eta = 0$$

or, going over to differences:
$$\sum_{A'D'} \frac{u_0 - u_1}{h}\,h = 0; \tag{22}$$

where u_0 denotes the values u on $A'D'$ and u_1 the values at the closest interior vertical.

From (20) and (22) it follows that

$$pC - \sum u_1 = 0$$

or
$$C = \frac{\sum u_1}{p} \tag{23}$$

where p denotes the number of summands in $\sum u_1$ (in other words, the number of horizontal rows in the network domain $A'B'F'E'D'$). Equation (23) enables C to be determined in the following manner by an iteration process. The value of the constant $C^{(n+1)}$ in the $(n+1)$-th approximation is determined from the equation

$$C^{(n+1)} = \frac{\sum u_1^{(n)}}{p}. \tag{24}$$

In Fig. 61a the solution of the problem set forth is carried out. In this solution, it is assumed that $m = \dfrac{90}{\pi}$ so that the value $\eta = 3$ corresponds to the value $\theta = \dfrac{\pi}{30}$. The values ξ are obtained thus: $\xi = \dfrac{90}{\pi}$ (log r — log 2.9); and they are recorded in the top line. The corresponding values r are in the lines beneath this; they were computed from the formula

$$r = 2{,}9\,e^{\frac{\pi\xi}{90}}$$

The constant C_1 in Formula (19) was established in such a way that the function u tends to zero at point B'. Fig. 61b shows the vicinity of the slot on a larger scale.

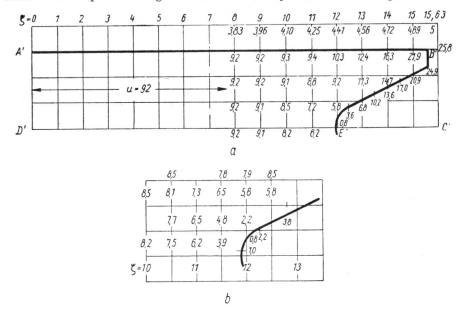

Fig. 61

5. Solution of the Laplace and Poisson Equations for an Inhomogeneous Medium

General Formulas. The method of differences is also well suited to the solution of the equation

$$\frac{\partial}{\partial x}\left(k\,\frac{\partial u}{\partial x}\right) + \frac{\partial}{\partial x}\left(k\,\frac{\partial u}{\partial y}\right) = f(x, y),$$

where k is a function of x and y. The complete solution runs exactly as for the usual Laplace equation, and only the formulas of Table 11 have to be replaced by others. We show these formulas in Table 17.

In this table, k_I, k_{II} etc. denote the function values k at the points I, II, etc. indicated in the patterns. These points lie at the middle of the respective intercepts between the points 0 and 1, 0 and 2, etc. The side of the square network is taken as equal to h.

TABLE 17

Formulas for the Solution of the Laplace and Poisson Equations
in the Case of an Inhomogeneous Medium

No.	Pattern	Formula
1		$u_0 = \dfrac{k_I u_1 + k_{II} u_2 + k_{III} u_2 + k_{IV} u_4}{k_I + k_{II} + k_{III} + k_{IV}} -$ $- \dfrac{h^2 f_0}{k_I + k_{II} + k_{III} + k_{IV}}$
2		$u_0 = \dfrac{k_V u_5 + k_{VI} u_6 + k_{VII} u_7 + k_{VIII} u_8}{k_V + k_{VI} + k_{VII} + k_{VIII}} -$ $- \dfrac{2 h^2 f_0}{k_V + k_{VI} + k_{VII} + k_{VIII}}$

IV. BIHARMONIC EQUATION

General Considerations

The biharmonic equation

$$\frac{\partial^4 u}{\partial x^4} + 2 \frac{\partial^4 u}{\partial x^2 \partial y^2} + \frac{\partial^4 u}{\partial y^4} = f(x, y)$$

may be solved by various methods, of which we will consider two:
1. Reduction to a system of Poisson equations,
2. Direct solution.

For numerical solution both methods can be used.

Reduction to a System of Poisson Equations. Clearly the equation

$$\frac{\partial^4 u}{\partial x^4} + 2 \frac{\partial^4 u}{\partial x^2 \partial y^2} + \frac{\partial^4 u}{\partial y^4} = f \tag{25}$$

can be replaced by the following system:

$$\left. \begin{array}{l} \dfrac{\partial^2 u}{\partial x^2} + \dfrac{\partial^2 u}{\partial y^2} = \varphi, \\[3mm] \dfrac{\partial^2 \varphi}{\partial x^2} + \dfrac{\partial^2 \varphi}{\partial y^2} = f. \end{array} \right\} \tag{26}$$

Due to this circumstance the same methods can be used for the approximate solution of boundary value problems for the biharmonic equation as were used for the Laplace and Poisson equations. We will solve such a boundary value problem for the biharmonic equation: On the boundary of a domain G the boundary values u_0 of the function u and the values of the derivative of its exterior normals $\dfrac{\partial u}{\partial n}$ are given. u should be determined in the interior of G. For a practical solution we proceed, as usual, from domain G to a network domain $\bar{G}$ and prepare two sets of traverses one according to Fig. 21c, the other according to Fig. 21d. In the traverses made according to Fig. 21d, we will write the values u and in those according to Fig. 21c the values φ. At the start of the computation we assume the initial values of u in the entire domain G, including its boundary (the values on the boundary are all equal to u_0). In addition, using the given values $\dfrac{\partial u}{\partial n}$, we find the values u in the next row of squares outside domain G by extrapolation. For this we use the relation

$$\frac{\partial u}{\partial n} = \frac{u_\nu}{h} = \frac{u_2 - u_0}{h}$$

(in which u_2 is the value of u in the next row of squares outward). From that we obtain

$$u_2 = u_0 + u_\nu \left(u_\nu \approx h \frac{\partial u}{\partial n} \right).$$

After getting the values u on the boundary and its adjacent rows (internally and externally) we can determine the values φ_0 of function φ on the $\bar{G}$-boundary, by starting from the relation

$$\varphi = \frac{\partial^2 u}{\partial x^2} + \frac{\partial^2 u}{\partial y^2}$$

and compute the right-hand member according to the formula

$$\varphi_0 = \frac{1}{h^2} \left[u_1 + u_2 + u_3 + u_4 - 4u_0 \right]$$

After determining the boundary values of function φ we can, by solving an ordinary Dirichlet problem, determine the values φ in the interior of G. When these values φ are found, we then refine the values u by Formula 1 of Table 11, since

$$\frac{\partial^2 u}{\partial x^2} + \frac{\partial^2 u}{\partial y^2} = \varphi$$

This necessarily signifies that:

$$u_0 = \frac{1}{4} \left[u_1 + u_2 + u_3 + u_4 - h^2 \varphi_0 \right].$$

On the right-hand side of this equation we insert the previous u-values and the values found for φ; on the left we obtain fresh improved u-values on the G-boundary. With the improved boundary values u we find improved boundary values φ, and with them new φ-values in the interior of the domain. With these values we again refine u, and so on. Since by this process we refine φ and u simultaneously, we finally reach systems of values which satisfy the difference equations obtained from equations (26); function u thereby satisfies equation (25) with the assumed boundary conditions.

Direct Solution. The direct solution is based on the differential equation (25) being replaced by a difference equation in accordance with one of the formulas shown in Table 18.

Examples

Example 1 ([G61], p. 145). Find a function v with the following properties: In the interior of a square it has to satisfy the biharmonic equation (25) with $f \equiv 0$ and on the boundary of the square v and $\frac{\partial v}{\partial n}$ are to assume given values.

In Fig. 62,0 the boundary values and the initial distribution of the function values v in the interior of the square are given. Plates 62,1—5 give the first two approximations for functions v and

$$\varphi = \frac{\partial^2 v}{\partial x^2} + \frac{\partial^2 v}{\partial y^2}.$$

Computation proceeds according to the method described above; the biharmonic equation is replaced by the system (26). To determine each succeeding approximation, a Dirichlet problem is solved. Fig. 62,6—7 give successive approximations and Fig. 62,8 shows the final solution.

TABLE 18

Formulas for Solution of the Biharmonic Equation

No.	Pattern	Formula
1		$$u_0 = \frac{8[u_1 + u_2 + u_3 + u_4] - 2[u_5 + u_6 + u_7 + u_8]}{20} - \\ - \frac{u_9 + u_{10} + u_{11} + u_{12}}{20} - \frac{h^4 f_0}{20}$$
2		$$u_0 = \frac{4\left(\frac{1}{a^2} + \frac{1}{b^2}\right)\left(\frac{u_2 + u_4}{a^2} + \frac{u_1 + u_3}{b^2}\right)}{6\left(\frac{1}{a^4} + \frac{1}{b^4}\right) + \frac{8}{a^2 b^2}} - \\ - \frac{\frac{2}{a^2 b^2}(u_5 + u_6 + u_7 + u_8)}{6\left(\frac{1}{a^4} + \frac{1}{b^4}\right) + \frac{8}{a^2 b^2}} - \\ - \frac{\frac{1}{a^4}(u_{10} + u_{12}) + \frac{1}{b^4}(u_9 + u_{11})}{6\left(\frac{1}{a^4} + \frac{1}{b^4}\right) + \frac{8}{a^2 b^2}} + \\ + \frac{f_0}{6\left(\frac{1}{a^4} + \frac{1}{b^4}\right) + \frac{8}{a^2 b^2}}$$

Example 2 ([G55], p. 60). Find the *deflection of a uniformly loaded square plate* resting freely on its edges.

Clearly this problem is reducible to the solution of equation (25) with $f \equiv$ const. or, what comes to the same thing, to the solution of the system

$$\frac{\partial^2 u}{\partial x^2} + \frac{\partial^2 u}{\partial y^2} = \varphi,$$

$$\frac{\partial^2 \varphi}{\partial x^2} + \frac{\partial^2 \varphi}{\partial y^2} = 1.$$

0

		0	0	10	20	30		
	0	0	10	20	30	40	50	
0	10	17	27	38	49	60	70	60
10	20	31	43	55	67	79	90	80
20	30	44	58	72	86	99	110	100
30	40	56	72	89	105	120	130	130
60	50	68	86	105	126	144	150	160
	60	80	100	120	150	180	170	
		70	90	120	160	190	v_0	

1

	27	7	8	9	—10	
—3	8	4	2	0	—6	—20
1	2	0	—3	—6	—12	—21
4	0	—3	—6	—10	—15	—21
6	—2	—7	—9	—12	—15	—10
8	—7	—12	—10	—15	—23	4
	—22	—24	—5	—14	—66	φ_0

3

	25	6	7	9	11	
—5	7	4	2	0	—3	—19
1	2	1	—2	—5	—10	—18
4	1	—2	—5	—8	—12	—18
7	1	—5	—7	—10	—12	—7
10	—5	—10	—7	—11	—18	10
	—20	—21	—2	—10	—60	φ_1

2

15	26	37	49	61
31	43	56	69	82
44	59	74	88	102
57	74	91	108	123
70	89	108	130	150

v_1

Fig. 62

4

15	25	37	49	61
30	43	56	70	83
44	59	75	90	104
58	75	93	110	126
70	90	109	132	150

v_2

5

	25	5	7	9	11	
—5	6	3	2	1	—4	—19
0	2	0	—2	—4	—9	—17
4	1	—2	—4	—7	—11	—18
7	0	—4	—6	—8	—10	—5
10	—5	—9	—7	—10	—18	10
	—20	—20	—1	—8	—60	φ_2

6

15	25	38	50	62
30	43	58	72	85
45	64	75	94	106
58	78	97	115	128
70	90	109	134	152

v_9

7

	25	5	8	10	12	
—5	7	4	3	2	—3	—18
0	2	1	—1	—3	—8	—16
5	1	—1	—3	—6	—9	—14
8	0	—4	—5	—7	—9	—2
11	—4	—8	—5	—9	—16	12
	—19	—18	2	—6	—58	φ_9

8

		0	0	10	20	30		
	0	0	10	20	30	40	50	
0	10	15	25	38	50	62	70	60
10	20	30	43	58	72	85	90	80
20	30	45	61	78	94	106	110	100
30	40	58	78	97	115	128	130	130
40	50	71	92	112	134	152	150	160
	60	80	100	120	150	180	170	
		70	90	120	160	190	v	

Fig. 62 (cont.)

For a definite working basis we make constant C equal to unity. For an unconstrained position of the plate, the boundary conditions give

$$u = \frac{\partial^2 u}{\partial n^2} = 0.$$ (27)

On the vertical side this gives

$$u = \frac{\partial^2 u}{\partial x^2} = 0\,;$$ (28)

since clearly also

$$\frac{\partial^2 u}{\partial y^2} = 0$$ (28′)

and

$$\varphi = \frac{\partial^2 u}{\partial x^2} + \frac{\partial^2 u}{\partial y^2}$$

we thus have in consequence of conditions (28) and (28′)

$$\varphi \equiv 0$$

on the vertical sides of the square.

A similar consideration evidently holds for the horizontal sides, only with the difference that here

$$\frac{\partial^2 u}{\partial n^2} = \frac{\partial^2 u}{\partial y^2}$$

Thus system (26) with boundary conditions (27) splits into two independent equations:

2) $$\frac{\partial^2 \varphi}{\partial x^2} + \frac{\partial^2 \varphi}{\partial y^2} = 1\,;$$ on the boundary,

1) $$\frac{\partial^2 u}{\partial x^2} + \frac{\partial^2 u}{\partial y^2} = \varphi\,;$$ on the boundary.

The solution of these equations is also effected in accordance with the methods described above. The results of the solution are set out in Fig. 63; because of symmetry only one eighth of the square is shown in the illustration.

0,000	0,071			
0,000	0,111	0,179		
0,000	0,132	0,215	0,261	
0,000	0,138	0,227	0,276	0,291

φ

0,0000	0,0106			
0,0000	0,0190	0,0342		
0,0000	0,0242	0,0437	0,0561	
0,0000	0,0260	0,0470	0,0603	0,0649

u

Fig. 63

V. THERMAL CONDUCTIVITY EQUATION

General Introductory Remarks

The approximate numerical solution of the heat conduction equation with given initial and boundary conditions[16]

$$\frac{\partial^2 u}{\partial x^2} = a^2 \frac{\partial u}{\partial t} \tag{29}$$

or

$$\frac{\partial^2 u}{\partial x^2} + \frac{\partial^2 u}{\partial y^2} = a^2 \frac{\partial u}{\partial t} \tag{29'}$$

to which, if u be regarded as temperature and t as duration, nonstationary heat problems are reducible, turns out to be simpler than the solution of the Laplace problem. The fundamental difference between these problems from the viewpoint of computation resides in the fact that the solution of the heat conduction equation is effected *without the aid of the method of successive approximations*. In order to keep operations more specific, we will discuss the solution of the equation with the initial condition

$$u(x, 0) = \varphi(x)$$

and the boundary conditions

$$u(0, t) = f_0(t),$$
$$u(L, t) = f_1(t)$$

If we replace the derivatives by differences, equation (29) becomes:

$$\frac{u_{i-1, k} - 2u_{ik} + u_{i+1, k}}{h^2} = a^2 \frac{u_{i, k+1} - u_{ik}}{l}. \tag{30}$$

Here h and l denote mesh widths for x and t respectively, and the notation

$$u_{ik} = u(ih, kl)$$

is introduced for the functional values.

By transformation of equation (30) we obtain

$$u_{i, k+1} = \left(1 - \frac{2l}{a^2 h^2}\right) u_{ik} + \frac{l}{a^2 h^2} (u_{i-1, k} + u_{i+1, k}). \tag{31}$$

If we consider this equation, we see: As soon as the function values at the points $i - 1$, i, $i + 1$ of row k are known, we can complete the value of the function at point i in the next row $(k + 1)$ (Fig. 64). As the values of the function in the lowest

---

[16] On this equation see, for instance, V. I. Smirnov, Course in Higher Mathematics, Vol. 2, or S. L. Sobolev [R42].

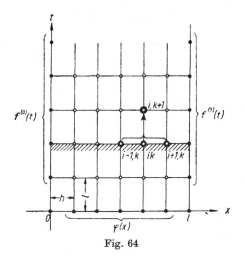

Fig. 64

row (for $t = 0$) are given, and as they are, moreover, known for the extreme verticals $x = 0$ and $x = L$, we can therefore, without any trouble, obtain the functional values u row by row by Formula (31). Similarly, also in the case of equation (29').

Formulas
for Solution of the Heat Conduction Equation

The formulas for the solution of the heat conduction equation are collected in Table 19. The formulas are accompanied by patterns, in which the t-axis points upward; the patterns are constructed axonometrically for three variables (x, y, t). u_i denotes the value of the function at point i of the pattern. Between the intervals in the directions of the x-, y-, and t-axes a relation is established which is likewise entered in the table. Formula 3 of Table 19 is obtained by means of a consideration analogous to those of Mikeladze ([R36], p. 83) that led to Formula 4. Using the equations

$$u_{i,k-1} = u_{ik} - l\,\frac{\partial u_{ik}}{\partial t} + \frac{l^2}{2}\,\frac{\partial^2 u_{ik}}{\partial t^2} + R_{ik}^{-},$$

$$u_{i,k+1} = u_{ik} + l\,\frac{\partial u_{ik}}{\partial t} + \frac{l^2}{2}\,\frac{\partial^2 u_{ik}}{\partial t^2} + R_{ik}^{+}$$

we arrive at the equation

$$\alpha u_{i,k-1} + \beta u_{i,k+1} - (a + \beta)u_{ik} =$$
$$= \frac{l}{a^2}\,(\beta - \alpha)\,\frac{\partial^2 u_{ik}}{\partial x^2} + \frac{l^2}{2a^4}\,(\beta + \alpha)\,\frac{\partial^4 u_{ik}}{\partial x^4} + R_{ik}.$$

Putting

$$\left.\begin{aligned}\frac{l}{a^2}\,(\beta - \alpha) &= h^2,\\[2mm]\frac{l^2}{2a^4}\,(\beta + \alpha) &= \frac{h^4}{12},\end{aligned}\right\} \tag{A}$$

we obtain $\alpha u_{i,k-1} + \beta u_{i,k+1} - (\alpha + \beta)\,u_{ik} \approx u_{i+1,k} - 2u_{ik} + u_{i-1,k}.$ (B)

The system of equations (A) can be written in the form

$$\beta - \alpha = \varepsilon,$$

$$\beta + \alpha = \frac{\varepsilon^2}{6}$$

in which $\varepsilon = \dfrac{a^2 h^2}{l}$. Solving this, we find

$$a = \frac{\varepsilon^2}{12} - \frac{\varepsilon}{2},$$

$$\beta = \frac{\varepsilon^2}{12} + \frac{\varepsilon}{2}.$$

Very simple values α and β are obtained on putting

$$\varepsilon = \frac{a^2 h^2}{l} = 6$$

Then $\alpha = 0,\ \beta = 6$, and from (B)

$$6u_{i,\,k+1} - 6u_{ik} \approx u_{i+1,\,k} - 2u_{ik} + u_{i-1,\,k},$$

whence it follows $\qquad u_{i,\,k+1} = \dfrac{u_{i+1,\,k} + 4u_{ik} + u_{i-1,\,k}}{6}.$

TABLE 19

I. $\dfrac{\partial^2 u}{\partial x^2} = a^2 \dfrac{\partial u}{\partial t}$ *Formulas for Solution of the Heat Conduction Equation*

No.	Pattern	Relation between l and h	Formula	Magnitude of error
1		arbitrary	$u_A = \left(1 - \dfrac{2l}{a^2 h^2}\right) u_0 +$ $+ \dfrac{l}{a^2 h^2}(u_1 + u_2)$	
2		$l = \dfrac{a^2 h^2}{2}$	$u_A = \dfrac{1}{2}(u_1 + u_2)$	h^2
3		$l = \dfrac{a^2 h^2}{6}$	$u_A = \dfrac{u_1 + 4u_0 + u_2}{6}$	h^1
4		$l = \dfrac{a^2 h^2}{16}$	$u_A = \dfrac{32u_B + 2u_0 + 3(u_1 + u_2)}{40}$	h^4

Continuation of Table 19

II. $\dfrac{\partial^2 u}{\partial x^2} + \dfrac{\partial^2 u}{\partial y^2} = a^2 \dfrac{\partial u}{\partial t}$

No.	Pattern	Relation between l and h	Formula	Magnitude of error
5		arbitrary	$u_A = \left(1 - \dfrac{4l}{a^2 h^2}\right) u_0 +$ $+ \dfrac{l}{a^2 h^2}(u_1 + u_2 + u_3 + u_4)$	
6		$l = \dfrac{a^2 h^2}{4}$	$u_A = \dfrac{1}{4}(u_1 + u_2 + u_3 + u_4)$	h^2
7		$l = \dfrac{a^2 h^2}{6}$	$u_A = \dfrac{16 u_0 + 4(u_1 + u_2 + u_3 + u_4)}{36} +$ $+ \dfrac{u_5 + u_6 + u_7 + u_8)}{36}$	h^4

Solution of the Heat Conduction Equation in a Triangular Network

Table 20 exhibits the formulas for the solution of the heat conduction equation for a network of equilateral triangles, as suggested by P. P. Yushkov [R45]. The t-axis points upward in the pattern.

TABLE 20

Formulas for Solution of the Heat Conduction Equation in a Triangular Network

No.	Pattern	Relation between l and h	Formula	Magnitude of error
1		arbitrary $l < \dfrac{a^2 h^2}{4}$	$u_A = \left(1 - \dfrac{4l}{a^2 h^2}\right) u_0 +$ $+ \dfrac{2l}{3 a^2 h^2}(u_1 + u_2 + u_3 + u_4 + u_5 + u_6)$	h^2
2		$l = \dfrac{a^2 h^2}{8}$	$u_A = \dfrac{1}{2} u_0 + \dfrac{1}{12}(u_1 + u_2 + u_3 + u_4 + u_5 + u_6)$	h^4

Refinement of Boundary Values

The refinement of boundary values is accomplished in a manner analogous to the solution of the Laplace and Poisson equations (see p. 38). The corresponding formula ([R37], p. 21) takes the form:

$$u_A = \frac{h}{2\delta} \frac{h\varphi_2 + \delta u_4}{h + \delta} + \frac{u_1 + u_3}{4} + u_0 \left(1 - \frac{h + \delta}{2\delta}\right).$$

The relation between l and h is $l = \dfrac{a^2 h^2}{4}.$

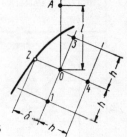

Fig. 65

The points 1, 2, 3, 4 are plotted in Fig. 65. φ_2 denotes, as before, the postulated size of function u on the actual boundary of the domain.

Mixed Type Boundary Conditions

Up to now the working of the solution for the heat conduction equation has been demonstrated when the *functional* values on the boundary were given. Often, a combination

$$au + b\frac{\partial u}{\partial n} = c \tag{32}$$

is postulated as boundary condition, where a and b are given functions of position (of the variables x, y) and of duration (of the variable t). In this type of problem, everything previously stated in regard to transfer of the boundary conditions to the boundary of the network domain, etc., is, of course, still in force.

We here mention only the characteristic peculiarities of such problems for the heat conduction equation, assuming that the condition (32) is already put down in the form

$$u_0 = \frac{c + \varkappa u_1}{a + \varkappa}$$

for the boundary of the network domain; for transformation into this form see Formula (13) above. Here u_0 denotes the value u at the boundary, and u_1 the value at the nearest interior point.

The working out of the solution proceeds as follows: We know the initial values at points 1, 2, 3, . . . (Fig. 66, for the sake of simplicity we consider the unidimensional case). From these we determine, by means of the general formulas, the functional values u at the interior points A_1, B_1, . . . of the first row (see Fig. 66). When we know the functional value u at point A_1 (say u_A), we determine the boundary value at point C_1 by Formula (13):

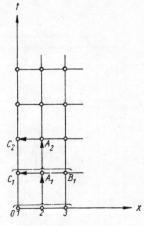

Fig. 66

$$u_c = \frac{c + \varkappa u_A}{a + \varkappa}.$$

After determination of these values we can find the values u at all interior points of the next row (at points A_2, B_2 etc.). For the computation at point A_2 we must use the boundary values just found. When the value u at point A_2 is found we must, again using Formula 13, find the boundary value at point C_2, etc. When a, b, c are dependent on x, y, and t, they then get their particular values for each boundary point and in each row.

Examples

Example 1. Solution of the Equation

$$\frac{\partial^2 u}{\partial x^2} + \frac{\partial^2 u}{\partial y^2} = \frac{\partial u}{\partial t}$$

for a square of 11 units length of side. The boundary and initial values are given in Fig. 67. The boundary values are constant. The solution is effected by Formula 16 of Table 19. The length of step for t is determined by the formula

$$l = \frac{a^2 h^2}{4}.$$

In our case $a = 1$. If we choose $h = 1$ (this choice corresponds to Fig. 67), we then get:
$$l = 0.25.$$

0	0	0	0	0	0	0	0	0	0		
7,82	7,11	6,40	5,69	4,98	4,27	3,55	2,84	2,13	1,42	0,61	0
15,45	14,05	12,64	11,24	9,83	8,43	7,02	5,62	4,21	2,81	1,42	0
22,70	20,64	18,57	16,51	14,45	12,38	10,32	8,25	6,20	4,21	2,13	0
29,39	26,72	24,05	21,37	18,70	16,03	13,36	10,69	8,25	5,62	2,84	0
35,36	32,15	28,93	25,72	22,50	19,29	16,07	13,36	10,32	7,02	3,55	0
40,45	36,20	32,60	29,05	25,80	22,55	19,29	16,03	12,38	8,43	4,27	0
44,55	40,80	37,05	33,30	29,55	25,80	22,50	18,70	14,45	9,83	4,98	0
47,56	44,00	40,44	36,88	33,30	29,05	25,75	21,37	16,51	11,24	5,69	0
49,38	46,40	43,42	40,44	37,05	32,60	28,93	24,05	18,57	12,64	6,40	0
50,00	48,20	46,40	44,00	40,80	36,20	32,15	26,72	20,64	14,05	7,11	0
	50,00	49,38	47,56	44,55	40,45	35,36	29,39	22,70	15,45	7,82	

Fig. 67

In Fig. 68 the solution is carried out for t from $t = 0.25$ to $t = 2.50$ (the temperature distribution for $t = 0.00$ is given in Fig. 67).

0,25

7,07	6,36	5,66	4,95	4,24	3,53	2,82	2,12	1,41	0,71
13,96	12,56	11,17	9,78	8,38	6,98	5,58	4,19	2,82	
20,51	18,46	16,41	14,36	12,31	10,25	8,21	6,23		
26,56	23,90	21,24	18,59	15,93	13,28	10,81			
31,80	28,63	25,46	22,38	19,29	16,32				
36,50	32,81	29,36	25,91	22,54					
40,44	36,78	33,13	29,55						
43,80	40,34	36,87							
46,25	43,42								
48,20									

0,50

7,04	6,32	5,62	4,92	4,22	3,51	2,81	2,10	1,41	0,70
13,90	12,48	11,10	9,72	8,33	6,94	5,55	4,19	2,80	
20,42	18,34	16,31	14,27	12,23	10,20	8,22	6,20		
26,40	23,72	21,09	18,48	15,87	13,33	10,74			
31,76	28,49	25,40	22,31	19,29	16,28				
36,38	32,82	29,33	25,96	22,60					
40,40	36,68	33,14	29,52						
43,65	40,22	36,74							
46,20	43,30								
48,12									

0,75

7,01	6,28	5,58	4,89	4,19	3,49	2,79	2,10	1,40	0,70
13,85	12,42	11,03	9,66	8,28	6,90	5,54	4,16	2,80	
20,34	18,23	16,20	14,18	12,17	10,18	8,17	6,20		
26,32	23,58	20,98	18,38	15,83	13,27	10,78			
31,66	28,43	25,30	22,28	19,26	16,31				
36,36	32,72	29,33	25,94	22,62					
40,32	36,64	33,07	29,55						
43,60	40,09	36,68							
46,11	43,21								
48,10									

Fig. 68

1,00

7,00	6,25	5,55	4,86	4,16	3,47	2,78	2,09	1,40	0,70
13,80	12,35	10,96	9,60	8,23	6,87	5,50	4,16	2,78	
20,28	18,12	16,10	14,10	12,12	10,13	8,18	6,16		
26,24	23,49	20,86	18,32	15,77	13,28	10,72			
31,62	28,34	25,26	22,22	19,26	16,26				
36,29	32,69	29,26	25,94	22,60					
40,29	36,55	33,05	29,55						
43,52	40,03	36,58							
46,07	43,10								
48,06									

1,25

6,97	6,22	5,52	4,85	4,14	3,45	2,76	2,08	1,39	0,70
13,77	12,28	10,90	9,57	8,19	6,83	5,50	4,13	2,78	
20,22	18,06	16,01	14,04	12,06	10,11	8,12	6,17		
26,20	23,39	20,79	18,24	15,74	13,22	10,73			
31,56	28,26	25,17	22,20	19,21	16,27				
36,26	32,61	29,27	25,91	22,60					
40,23	36,52	32,98	29,50						
43,49	39,94	36,54							
46,02	43,05								
48,04									

1,50

6,95	6,19	5,50	4,81	4,12	3,43	2,76	2,07	1,39	0,70
13,73	12,24	10,84	9,50	8,15	6,81	5,46	4,13	2,76	
20,18	17,95	15,95	13,97	12,02	10,06	8,13	6,13		
26,14	23,35	20,70	18,19	15,68	13,21	10,67			
31,52	28,18	25,13	22,13	19,20	16,22				
36,21	32,58	29,17	25,89	22,56					
40,20	36,44	32,96	29,44						
43,44	39,90	36,46							
45,99	42,98								
48,01									

Fig. 68 (Continued)

1,75

6,94	6,17	5,46	4,78	4,10	3,42	2,74	2,07	1,38	0,70
13,70	12,18	10,80	9,44	8,11	6,78	5,46	4,10	2,76	
20,13	17,93	15,87	13,92	11,96	10,04	8,08	6,13		
26,11	23,24	20,66	18,12	15,66	13,16	10,67			
31,47	28,14	25,04	22,10	19,15	16,20				
36,19	32,50	29,14	25,82	22,54					
40,16	36,41	32,88	29,42						
43,41	39,83	36,43							
45,95	42,94								
48,00									

2,00

6,92	6,14	5,44	4,75	4,08	3,40	2,74	2,06	1,38	0,69
13,68	12,15	10,74	9,40	8,07	6,76	5,42	4,10	2,74	
20,11	17,86	15,83	13,85	11,93	10,00	8,08	6,09		
26,06	23,21	20,57	18,08	15,60	13,14	10,62			
31,45	28,06	25,01	22,03	19,12	16,16				
36,14	32,47	29,06	25,80	22,48					
40,14	36,34	32,85	29,35						
43,38	39,80	36,36							
45,93	42,89								
47,98									

2,25

6,91	6,13	5,41	4,73	4,06	3,40	2,72	2,06	1,37	0,69
13,66	12,10	10,70	9,35	8,04	6,72	5,42	4,08	2,74	
20,08	17,82	15,76	13,81	11,88	9,98	8,03	6,09		
26,04	23,14	20,53	18,01	15,57	13,10	10,61			
31,40	28,04	24,93	22,00	19,07	16,13				
36,13	32,40	29,03	25,73	22,46					
40,10	36,32	32,78	29,32						
43,36	39,74	36,32							
45,91	42,86								
47,96									

Fig. 68 (Continued)

2,50

6,90	6,10	5,39	4,70	4,04	3,39	2,72	2,04	1,37	0,68
13,64	12,08	10,66	9,32	8,00	6,71	5,29	4,08	2,72	
20,06	17,77	15,72	13,75	11,85	9,93	8,02	6,06		
26,00	23,11	20,46	17,98	15,52	13,07	10,56			
31,39	27,97	24,90	21,94	19,04	16,08				
36,09	32,38	28,96	25,70	22,40					
40,09	36,26	32,75	29,26						
43,33	39,72	36,26							
45,89	42,82								
47,96									

Fig. 68 (End)

Example 2 ([R36], p. 85). *Solution of the Equation*

$$\frac{\partial u}{\partial t} = 1{,}1\,\frac{\partial^2 u}{\partial x^2}$$

for a rod 44 cm. long. For $t = 0$, the temperature along the rod is distributed according to the law

$$u = 5 \sin \frac{\pi x}{44}$$

At the extremities of the rod, the temperature is kept constant at $u = 0$.

We shall effect the solution by Formula 4 of Table 19. If we put $h = 8.8$, $\frac{1}{a^2} = 1.1$, then from the formula

$$l = \frac{a^2 h^2}{16}$$

we find for l the value $l = 4.4$.

As the values u for *two* preceding rows must be known for the computation by Formula 4 of Table 19, we calculate the value u for row 4.4 by Formula 2 of Table 19;

44 0	0	2,296	3,715	3,715	2,296	0
39,6	0	2,353	3,808	3,808	2,353	0
35,2	0	2,412	3,903	3,903	2,412	0
30,8	0	2,472	4,001	4,001	2,472	0
26,4	0	2,534	4,101	4,101	2,534	0
22,0	0	2,597	4,203	4,203	2,597	0
17,6	0	2,662	4,308	4,308	2,662	0
13,2	0	2,729	4,416	4,416	2,729	0
8,8	0	2,797	4,526	4,526	2,797	0
4,4	0	2,867	4,639	4,639	2,867	0
$t = 0$	0	2,939	4,755	4,755	2,939	0
	$x = 0$	8,8	17,6	26,4	35,2	44,0

Fig. 69

in order not to lose any accuracy by this, we make the scale smaller here and actually put $h = 2.2$. Then from the relation

$$l = \frac{a^2 h^2}{2}$$

we obtain also　　　　　　　　　　　$l = 2.2.$

We can obtain the value of u for $t = 4.4$ by using Formula 2 of Table 19 twice. After we have the value u for $t = 4.4$, further computation is very easily performed. It is shown in Fig. 69. The computation is carried through as far as $t = 44.0$.

Example 3. *Improvement of Boundary Values. Solution of the Equation*

$$\frac{\partial^2 u}{\partial x^2} + \frac{\partial^2 u}{\partial y^2} = 4 \frac{\partial u}{\partial t}$$

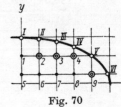

Fig. 70

for the ellipse　　　　　　　　　$4 x^2 + 16 y^2 = 1.$

On the ellipse we have　　　　　$u = e^{-0.5 t} \cos x \cos y.$

The initial values are　　　　　$u(x, y, 0) = \cos x \cos y.$

Because of symmetry it is sufficient to indicate the solution for one quarter of the ellipse (Fig. 70). The coordinates of points I—VI have to be determined. The boundary values at these points will be computed by the formula by which the function u is fixed at the boundary. The mesh width on the xy-plane is chosen equal to 0.1, i.e. $h = 0.1$. The length of step for t is determined from the relation

$$l = \frac{a^2 h^2}{4} = \frac{4 \cdot 0.01}{4} = 0.01$$

The values of u at points 1, 5, 6, 7, 8 are calculated by Formula 6 of Table 19, those at points 2, 3, 4, 9 by formula on page 88. In Fig. 71, the solutions up to $t = 0.1$ are shown. On the final traverse ($t = 0.1$) the exact solution for $t = 0.1$ is shown in parentheses for comparison purposes.

I	II	III	IV	$t = 0$ (Starting value)	
0,96891	0,96530	0,95446	0,93630		
1	2	3	4	V	
0,98877	0,98383	0,96906	0,94431	0,91072	
5	6	7	8	9	VI
0,99875	0,99376	0,97884	0,95415	0,91991	0,88128

Fig. 71

I	II	III	IV	$t = 0,01$	
0,96408	0,96048	0,94970	0,93163		
1	2	3	4	V	
0,98383	0,97893	0,96423	0,93991	0,90618	
5	6	7	8	9	VI
0,99376	0,98880	0,97395	0,94938	0,91532	0,87688

I	II	III	IV	$t = 0,02$	
0,95927	0,95570	0,94496	0,92698		
1	2	3	4	V	
0,97892	0,97403	0,95942	0,93519	0,90166	
5	6	7	9	9	VI
0,98880	0,98386	0,96909	0,94464	0,91074	0,87251

I	II	III	IV	$t = 0,03$	
0,95448	0,95093	0,94025	0,92236		
1	2	3	4	V	
0,97403	0,96917	0,95462	0,93054	0,89716	
5	6	7	8	9	VI
0,98386	0,97894	0,96425	0,93992	0,90620	0,86816

I	II	III	IV	$t = 0,04$	
0,94973	0,94619	0,94556	0,91776		
1	2	3	4	V	
0,96917	0,96433	0,94986	0,92589	0,89269	
5	6	7	8	9	VI
0,97894	0,97406	0,95943	0,93523	0,90168	0,86383

Fig. 71 (Continued)

$t = 0,05$

I	II	III	IV		
0,94499	0,94147	0,93089	0,91318		
1	2	3	4	V	
0,96433	0,95952	0,94512	0,92128	0,88823	
5	6	7	8	9	VI
0,97406	0,96919	0,95464	0,93056	0,89718	0,85952

$t = 0,06$

I	II	III	IV		
0,94028	0,93678	0,92626	0,90863		
1	2	3	4	V	
0,95952	0,95473	0,94040	0,91667	0,88381	
5	6	7	8	9	VI
0,96919	0,96435	0,94988	0,92952	0,89270	0,85524

$t = 0,07$

I	II	III	IV		
0,93559	0,93210	0,92164	0,90410		
1	2	3	4	V	
0,95473	0,94996	0,93571	0,91211	0,87940	
5	6	7	8	9	VI
0,96435	0,95954	0,94514	0,92129	0,88825	0,85097

$t = 0,08$

I	II	III	IV		
0,93092	0,92745	0,91704	0,89959		
1	2	3	4	V	
0,94996	0,94522	0,93104	0,90755	0,87501	
5	6	7	8	9	VI
0,95954	0,95475	0,94042	0,91670	0,88382	0,84673

Fig. 71 (Continued)

I	II	III	IV	$t = 0,09$	
0,92628	0,92283	0,91246	0,89510		
1	2	3	4	V	
0,94522	0,94051	0,92639	0,90303	0,87065	
5	6	7	8	9	VI
0,95475	0,94998	0,93573	0,91212	0,87941	0,84250

I	II	III	IV	$t = 0,10$	
0,92166	0,91822	0,90791	0,89064		
1	2	3	4	V	
0,94050	0,93581	0,92178	0,89852	0,86630	
(0,94055)	(0,93585)	(0,92180)	(0,89854)		
5	6	7	8	9	VI
0,94988	0,94524	0,93106	0,90757	0,87502	0,83830
(0,95004)	(0,94529)	(0,93111)	(0,90761)	(0,87504)	

Fig. 71 (End)

VI. WAVE AND TELEGRAPH EQUATIONS

General Remarks

For the solution of equations of the hyperbolic type, the method of differences is used far more rarely than in the solution of the elliptic or parabolic types. This is quite understandable, since hyperbolic equations can often be solved very successfully by other methods. However, in many cases the method of differences is also of service; we will now discuss this, though not to so great an extent as we did with the other equations.

Take the wave equation
$$\frac{\partial^2 u}{\partial t^2} = a^2 \frac{\partial^2 u}{\partial x^2} \tag{33}$$

with the initial conditions
$$u = f(x), \quad \frac{\partial u}{\partial t} = \varphi(x)$$

for $t = 0$ and the boundary conditions
$$u(0, t) = F(t), \quad u(L, t) = \Phi(t).$$

On transition to the difference equation we immediately determine a fixed relation between the intervals for x and t, by putting
$$l = \frac{h}{a} \tag{34}$$

(see [G49]).

If we plot the relative network, the diagonals of the rectangles will run straight along the characteristics of the equation under consideration, which are clearly given by the formula
$$x \pm at = \text{const}$$

Proceeding from equation (33) to the corresponding difference equation. we obtain
$$\frac{u_{i, k+1} - 2u_{ik} + u_{i, k-1}}{l^2} = a^2 \frac{u_{i+1, k} - 2u_{ik} + u_{i-1, k}}{h^2},$$

from which, taking account of (34), equation (33) becomes
$$u_{i, k+1} = u_{i+1, k} + u_{i-1, k} - u_{i, k-1} \tag{35}$$

This equation is the difference equation. In Fig. 72 the road to its solution is mapped out. This pattern shows how each new u-value is formed; especially can one see from this that for the formation of the u-value of a row, the values from *two* anterior rows are used, in contrast to the heat conduction equation where a *single* row was sufficient (see Fig. 64). To start the computation it is likewise necessary to know u in two rows. This is obtained from the fact that for $t = 0$, the function $u = f(x)$ and the derivative

$$\frac{\partial u}{\partial t} = \varphi(x) \tag{36}$$

are given. Substituting relation (36) by the difference equation, we get for point $x = hi$

$$\frac{u_{i,-1} - u_{i0}}{l} = \varphi_i,$$

whence follows $\qquad u_{i,-1} = u_{i0} + l\varphi_i \tag{37}$

Formula (37) gives the values of u in the second row [row (—1) in Fig. 72]. Having these as well as the u-values in row (0), one can start right away with the computations. Instead of using this method, one can also calculate the values in row (+1) by means of the Taylor formula. This method is similarly preferable in cases when the analytic expressions for the functions $f(x)$ and $\varphi(x)$ are known. As far as the boundary conditions are concerned, everything that was said regarding the heat conduction equation still holds word for word here.

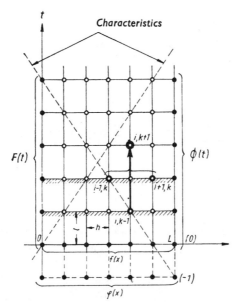

Fig. 72

In the wave equation example the specific peculiarities of the setting and solution of the problem for the determination of the integral of a hyperbolic equation are quite obvious. It is easy to see, for instance, that when the boundary and initial values are given at the points marked in black in Fig. 73 the solution can be determined in domain A which is marked out with white dots in the illustration. This domain is bounded by the characteristics passing through the latter points with known boundary values on the straight verticals (see [R42]). It is likewise easy to see that the problem of determining the function u that satisfies equation (35) at the lattice points can be solved in similar fashion also in the case when the u-values are given on two character-istics (Fig. 74); in this case the solution is determined in domain A. Finally, it should be noted that when the solution of equation (35) is found in some domain A (Fig. 75) that is bounded not by characteristics but by other lines, the solution can be completed by determining it in that partial domain A' obtained when the characteristics are drawn through the outermost parts of domain A. In this case the value of function u at point $(i + 1, k)$ is found from the values in the vicinity (Fig. 75) from the formula

$$u_{i+1, k} = u_{i, k+1} + u_{i, k-1} - u_{i-1, k}$$

which follows from Formula (35).

We are here investigating the solution of the wave equation. The telegrapher's equation

$$\frac{\partial^2 w}{\partial x^2} = a^2 \frac{\partial^2 w}{\partial t^2} + b^2 \frac{\partial w}{\partial t} + c^2 w \qquad (b^4 - 4a^2 c^2 > 0) \tag{38}$$

passes, after the transformation $w(x, t) = e^{-\frac{b^2}{2 a^2} \cdot t} u(x, t)$ \hfill (39)

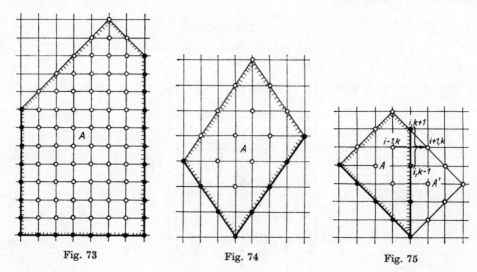

Fig. 73   Fig. 74   Fig. 75

into the equation

$$\frac{\partial^2 u}{\partial x^2} = a^2 \frac{\partial^2 u}{\partial t^2} - \gamma^2 u \tag{40}$$

where

$$\gamma^2 = \frac{b^4}{4 a^2} - c^2 \tag{41}$$

The solution of equation (40) is effected in exactly the same manner as the solution of equation (33), except that the difference equation (35) looks slightly different (see Table 21).

Formulas for the Solution of the Wave and Telegrapher's Equations

In Table 21 the formulas for the solution of the wave and telegrapher's equations are given. The formulas are accompanied by patterns in which the t-axis is directed upward; u_i denotes the value of the function at point i. The telegrapher's equation is assumed to be in form (40). The ratio between the intervals for x and t respectively is given by equation (34).

TABLE 21

Formulas for the Solution of the Wave and Telegrapher's Equations

No.	Equation	Pattern	Relation between l and h	Formula	Magnitude of error
1	$\dfrac{\partial^2 u}{\partial t^2} = a^2 \dfrac{\partial^2 u}{\partial x^2}$		$l = \dfrac{h}{a}$	$u_A = u_1 + u_2 - u_3$	h^2
2	$\dfrac{\partial^2 u}{\partial t^2} = a^2 \dfrac{\partial^2 u}{\partial x^2} +$ $+ b^2 u$		$l = \dfrac{h}{a}$	$u_A = u_1 +$ $+ u_2 - u_3 + \dfrac{b^2 h^2}{a^2} u_0$	h^2

Example ([R36], p. 60) Solution of the equation

$$\frac{\partial^2 u}{\partial t^2} = \frac{\partial^2 u}{\partial x^2}$$

with boundary conditions $u(0, t) = u(\pi, t) = 0$

and initial conditions
$$\left. \begin{array}{l} u = x(\pi - x) \\[2mm] \dfrac{\partial u}{\partial t} = 0 \end{array} \right\} \quad \text{for } t = 0.$$

We choose $h = l = \dfrac{\pi}{18}$. We compute the values u_{i1} in the row $t = \dfrac{\pi}{18}$ by the Taylor formula, putting $u_{i1} \approx u_{i0} + h \dfrac{\partial u_{i0}}{\partial t} + \dfrac{h^2}{2} \dfrac{\partial^2 u_{i0}}{\partial t^2}$

and taking into account, from the given equation,

$$\frac{\partial^2 u_{i0}}{\partial t^2} = \frac{\partial^2 u_{i0}}{\partial x^2}$$

Thus $u_{i1} = u_{i0} - h^2 = u_{i0} - 0{,}03046$.

The solution is carried further by Formula 1 of Table 21. It is shown in Fig. 76 where, on account of symmetry, only half of the strip from $x = 0$ to $x = \dfrac{\pi}{2}$ is represented. Further examples are to be found in Mikeladze's book [R36] and in Gavrilov's papers [R27] and [R28].

	$x=0$	h	2 h	3 h	4 h	5 h	6 h	7 h	8 h	9 h
9 h	0	0	0,00001	— 0,00001	0,00003	— 0,00002	0,00004	— 0,00002	0,00005	— 0,00002
8 h	0	0,06093	0,12184	0,18279	0,24368	0,30465	0,36552	0,42651	0,48737	0,51790
7 h	0	0,12184	0,24371	0,36553	0,48741	0,60922	0,73112	0,85291	0,94436	0,97476
6 h	0	0,18278	0,36553	0,54833	0,73107	0,91388	1,09661	1,24897	1,34030	1,37082
5 h	0	0,24369	0,48740	0,73107	0,97480	1,21846	1,43173	1,58400	1,67543	1,70584
4 h	0	0,30462	0,60923	0,91387	1,21846	1,49265	1,70585	1,85819	1,94954	1,98004
3 h	0	0,36554	0,73109	1,09662	1,43172	1,70585	1,91911	2,07139	2,16280	2,19324
2 h	0	0,42647	0,85293	1,24894	1,58401	1,85818	2,07139	2,22372	2,31509	2,34556
h	0	0,48739	0,94432	1,34032	1,67540	1,94955	2,16279	2,31509	2,40648	2,43694
$t=0$	0	0,51785	0,97478	1,37078	1,70586	1,98001	2,19325	2,34555	2,43694	2,46740

Fig. 76

VII. QUASILINEAR HYPERBOLIC SYSTEMS

General Remarks

A large number of problems of significant theoretic and practical interest lead to the solution of systems of differential equations of the form

$$a_{11}\frac{\partial u}{\partial x} + a_{12}\frac{\partial v}{\partial x} + b_{11}\frac{\partial u}{\partial y} + b_{12}\frac{\partial v}{\partial y} = e_1,$$

$$a_{21}\frac{\partial u}{\partial x} + a_{22}\frac{\partial v}{\partial y} + b_{21}\frac{\partial u}{\partial y} + b_{22}\frac{\partial v}{\partial y} = e_2, \qquad (42)$$

where a_{11}, a_{12}, b_{11}, . . . , b_{22}, e_1, e_2 are functions of x, y, u, v. Equations of the form (42) are called *quasilinear*. (If the coefficients a_{11}, . . ., e_2 do not depend on u and v, the equations become quite linear [G50], p. 35.) If, in these circumstances, in one domain of the values x, y, u, v the roots χ_1 and χ_2 of the equation

$$\begin{vmatrix} b_{11} - a_{11}\chi & b_{12} - a_{12}\chi \\ b_{21} - a_{21}\chi & b_{22} - a_{22}\chi \end{vmatrix} = 0 \qquad (43)$$

are real and different, then the equations (42) are called *hyperbolic* equations in this domain ([R32], p. 39). The solution of a quasilinear hyperbolic equation of the form (42) can be reduced to the integration of equations of the *characteristics* which are defined in manner known (see [R32], p. 41 et seq., and [R33], p. 41 et seq.).

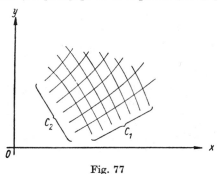

Fig. 77

The equations of the characteristics have the form

$$dy = \chi_1 dx; \; (E + A\chi_1)\, du + D\, dv + M\, dx + N\, dy = 0,$$

$$dy = \chi_2 dx; \; (E + A\chi_2)\, du + D\, dv + M\, dx + N\, dy = 0, \qquad (44)$$

where χ_1 and χ_2 are the roots of equation (43) and the coefficients E, A, ..., N are given by the formulas

$$E = \begin{vmatrix} b_{12}\, a_{11} \\ b_{22}\, a_{21} \end{vmatrix}; \quad A = \begin{vmatrix} a_{11}\, a_{12} \\ b_{21}\, a_{22} \end{vmatrix}; \quad D = \begin{vmatrix} b_{21}\, a_{12} \\ b_{22}\, a_{22} \end{vmatrix};$$

$$M = \begin{vmatrix} e_1\, b_{12} \\ e_2\, b_{22} \end{vmatrix}; \quad N = \begin{vmatrix} a_{12}\, e_1 \\ a_{22}\, e_2 \end{vmatrix}$$

The equations

$$dy = \chi_1\, dx,$$
$$dy = \chi_2\, dx$$

determine two families of curves C_1 and C_2 (Fig. 77) in the xy-plane. These curves are called the characteristics, belonging to the first or second family, and the differential equations

$$(E + A\chi_1)\, du + D\, dv + M\, dx + N\, dy = 0,$$
$$(E + A\chi_2)\, du + D\, dv + M\, dx + N\, dy = 0$$

are called the differential relations holding along the characteristics of the first or second family. In order to obtain a completely determinate solution of the system of equations (42), it is necessary to postulate supplementary conditions that can be of a different nature. Dependent on these conditions, different problems are distinguished for the equations (42); thus, e.g.:

a) The Cauchy Problem. On a smooth arc AB of a curve cut once only by each characteristic of the first and second families (Fig. 78) the values of the functions u and v are given

$$u = f_1(s),$$
$$v = f_2(s)$$

$f_1(s)$ and $f_2(s)$ here denote functions of the arc AB to be measured along s, which should have continuous derivatives of the first order. The solution is determined in the curvilinear quadrilateral $ACBD$, formed by the arcs of the characteristics of both families, which go through the terminal points of curve AB.

b) The Riemann Problem. On arcs CA and CB of the characteristics of the first and second families, the values of the functions u and v

$$u = \varphi_1(\xi); \qquad u = \varphi_2(\eta);$$
$$v = \psi_1(\xi); \qquad v = \psi_2(\eta)$$

are given (Fig. 79). The functions $\varphi_1(\xi)$ and $\psi_1(\xi)$ of the arc ξ to be measured along the characteristic CA of the first family and the functions $\varphi_2(\eta)$ and $\psi_2(\eta)$ of the arc η to be measured along the characteristic CB of the second family should possess continuous derivatives of the first order and have equal values at point C. If the arcs ξ and η are measured from C, then

$$\varphi_1(0) = \varphi_2(0),$$
$$\psi_1(0) = \psi_2(0).$$

The solution is determined in the quadrilateral $CADB$ formed by the arcs CA and CB with the arcs running through the points A and B.

c) Mixed Problems. Combinations of the conditions for the Cauchy and Riemann problems are possible: The values u and v on a characteristic and on an arc of a curve which is not a characteristic are given, or combinations of the functions u and v are given. All such problems are known as mixed problems.

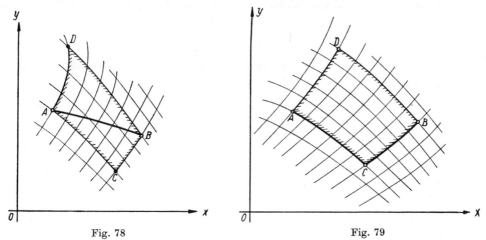

Fig. 78   Fig. 79

Approximate solution

The system of equations (44) whose solution is equivalent to the solution of system (42) can be solved by plotting the network of the characteristics and computation of the values of u and v at the lattice points from the differential relations. This method, originated by Massau [R38], was significantly perfected by Khristianovich and used by Khristianovich, Sokolovsky [R43], [R44], and others for the solution of a series of problems.

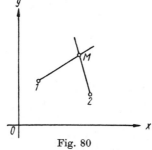

Fig. 80

a) *General Procedure.* At points 1 and 2 (Fig. 80) on the xy-plane all necessary magnitudes are known, i.e. x_1, y_1, u_1, v_1, and x_2, y_2, u_2, v_2. Point M is determined as the intersection of the straight lines running through points 1 and 2 with the same inclinations as the pertinent characteristics. The coordinates x_M, y_M of point M are found consequently from the equations

$$y_M - y_1 = \chi_1(x_1, y_1)(x_M - x_1),$$
$$y_M - y_2 = \chi_2(x_2, y_2)(x_M - x_2)$$

which replace the equations

$$dy = \chi_1 dx;$$
$$dy = \chi_2 dx$$

Then from the differential relationships

$$(E + A\chi_1)\, du + D\, dv + M\, dx + N\, dy = 0,$$
$$(E + A\chi_2)\, du + D\, dv + M\, dx + N\, dy = 0,$$

by replacing the differentials by differences, we obtain for the determination of u_M and v_M the equations

$$[E_1 + A_1\chi_1(x_1, y_1)]\,(u_M - u_1) + D_1(v_M - v_1) + M_1(x_M - x_1) + N_1(y_M - y_1) = 0,$$
$$[E_2 + A_2\chi_2(x_2, y_2)]\,(u_M - u_2) + D_2(v_M - v_2) + M_2(x_M - x_2) + N_2(y_M - y_2) = 0.$$

Thus all the necessary quantities x_M, y_M, u_M, v_M are specified at point M.

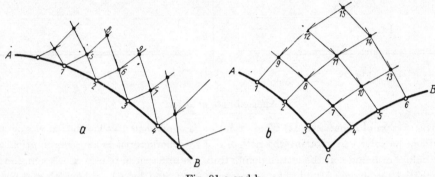

Fig. 81 a and b

The determination of the further points is carried out in a different manner according to the particular problem to be solved.

In the case of the solution of the Cauchy problem (Fig. 81a) the computation is effected as follows: The data at the points of curve AB and hence at points 1, 2, 3, 4 are known. From points 1, 2 we determine, as described above, the data at point 5, from points 2, 3 those for point 6, from points 3, 4 those for point 7; then similarly from points 5, 6 for point 8, from points 6, 7 for point 9, and so on.

In the case of the Riemann problem (Fig. 81b) the values of u and v on the characteristics CA and CB, i.e. at the points 1, 2, 3, 4, 5, 6 are known. From points 3, 4 we determine point 7, from points 2, 7 point 8, from points 1, 8 point 9. Then similarly we proceed to the second row and determine point 10 from points 7, 5, point 11 from points 8, 10, and so on.

In the case of mixed problems the two processes must be combined.

b) *Improvement of accuracy of the computations.* When the data are determined for point M, the computation can be repeated by using the equations

$$y'_M - y_1 = \chi'_1(x'_M - x_1),$$
$$y'_M - y_2 = \chi'_2(x'_M - x_2)$$

in which the quantities χ_1 and χ_2 are taken not for the starting values x_1, y_1, u_1, v_1, and x_2, y_2, u_2, v_2, but for the corrected values

$$x_1' = \frac{1}{2}(x_1 + x_M), \qquad\qquad x_2' = \frac{1}{2}(x_2 + x_M),$$

$$y_1' = \frac{1}{2}(y_1 + y_M), \qquad\qquad y_2' = \frac{1}{2}(y_2 + y_M),$$

$$u_1' = \frac{1}{2}(u_1 + u_M), \qquad\qquad u_2' = \frac{1}{2}(u_2 + u_M),$$

$$v_1' = \frac{1}{2}(v_1 + v_M), \qquad\qquad v_2' = \frac{1}{2}(v_2 + v_M)$$

If $\qquad\qquad x_M' = x_M, \qquad y_M' = y_M$

within the limits of accuracy, then the computation of x_M and y_M is to be considered as final. Otherwise the process of computation is repeated.

c) *Computation formulas.* The principal arithmetical operation in the method under consideration is the solution of a system of two linear equations of the form

$$y_M - y_1 = \chi_1(x_M - x_1),$$
$$y_M - y_2 = \chi_2(x_M - x_2).$$

It is effected by the formulas adduced in Table 22.

TABLE 22

Pattern	Formula	Note
	1) $\quad x_M = \dfrac{\chi_2 x_2 - \chi_1 x_1 - y_2 + y_1}{\chi_2 - \chi_1}$ 2) $\quad y_M = y_1 + \chi_1(x_M - x_1)$ or $\quad y_M = y_2 + \chi_2(x_M - x_2)$	First of all x_M is computed; this value is then used in the computation of y_M.

Examples

Example 1 ([R33], p. 121). Computation of the reflected wave in a channel, neglecting friction.

The equations of non-steady motion in the absence of drag take the form

$$\begin{cases} \dfrac{\partial U}{\partial t} + U\dfrac{\partial U}{\partial s} = -\dfrac{g}{B}\dfrac{\partial F}{\partial s}, \\[2mm] \dfrac{\partial F}{\partial t} + \dfrac{\partial(UF)}{\partial s} = 0. \end{cases} \qquad (45)$$

Here U is the mean velocity, F the area of the effective cross section, B the width of free surface, s the distance measured along the channel, t the time.

We rearrange system (45) into the form

$$\frac{\partial U}{\partial t} + U \frac{\partial u}{\partial s} + \frac{g}{B} \frac{\partial F}{\partial s} = 0,$$

$$\frac{\partial F}{\partial t} + F \frac{\partial U}{\partial s} + U \frac{\partial F}{\partial s} = 0.$$

Employing at the same time the general rule for obtaining characteristics (see p. 103), we can put

$$a_{11} = 1; \qquad a_{12} = 0; \qquad b_{11} = U; \qquad b_{12} = \frac{g}{B},$$

$$a_{21} = 0; \qquad a_{22} = 1; \qquad b_{21} = F: \qquad b_{22} = U.$$

The equation for determining functions χ_1 and χ_2 is written thus:

$$\chi^2 - 2U\chi + \left(U^2 - \frac{gF}{B}\right) = 0.$$

This equation has roots

$$\chi_1 = U + \sqrt{\frac{gF}{B}},$$

$$\chi_2 = U - \sqrt{\frac{gF}{B}}.$$

The coefficients A, E, D, M, N have the following values:

$$A = 1; E = -U; D = \frac{g}{B}; M = N = 0,$$

and the equations of the characteristics run thus:

$$\text{(I)} \quad \begin{cases} ds = \left(U + \sqrt{\frac{gF}{B}}\right) dt, \\[2ex] \sqrt{\frac{gF}{B}} \, dU + \frac{g}{B} \, dF = 0, \end{cases}$$

$$\text{(II)} \quad \begin{cases} ds = \left(U - \sqrt{\frac{gF}{B}}\right) dt, \\[2ex] -\sqrt{\frac{gF}{B}} \, dU + \frac{g}{B} \, dF = 0. \end{cases}$$

The differential relations can clearly be put in the form

$$dU + \sqrt{\frac{g}{BF}} \, dF = 0,$$

$$dU - \sqrt{\frac{g}{BF}} \, dF = 0,$$

or, introducing the function

$$\lambda(F) = \int_0^F \sqrt{\frac{g}{BF}}\, dF$$

into the form
$$dU + d\lambda = 0,$$
$$dU - d\lambda = 0$$

Using the notations
$$U + \lambda = \xi, \quad U - \lambda = \eta \tag{46}$$

or
$$U = \frac{1}{2}(\xi + \eta),$$

$$\lambda = \frac{1}{2}(\xi - \eta),$$

we ultimately write the differential relations in the form
$$d\xi = 0; \quad d\eta = 0.$$

whence it follows that
$$\xi = \text{const},$$
$$\eta = \text{const}.$$

Thus finally the problem is reduced to the integration of the equations

$$\left.\begin{array}{ll} ds = \left(U + \sqrt{\dfrac{gF}{B}}\right) dt, & \xi = \text{const} \\[3mm] ds = \left(U - \sqrt{\dfrac{gF}{B}}\right) dt, & \eta = \text{const} \end{array}\right\} \tag{47}$$

where ξ and η are defined by the equations (46).

Clearly in these equations, it is more advantageous to regard ξ and η as independent variables, whereupon the equations on the right can further be regarded as equations of the characteristics and those on the left as differential relationships.

Considering a channel of rectangular cross section, then
$$B = \text{const.},$$
$$F = BH,$$
where H is the head of water in the channel. The function λ is determined by the formula
$$\lambda = 2\sqrt{gH}$$

The problem underlying the solution is formulated thus: In a channel 1 m. wide, a wall stands at a distance of 5000 meters from the end of the channel (Fig. 82). The depth of water in front of the wall amounts to 2.2 m., behind the wall it is 1.2 m. The wall is demolished at time $t = 0$. At the extremity of the channel runs a backwash from the lowering of the water level, and this is reflected, after arrival at the extremity $s = 0$, in the positive direction of the s-axis. Required, the computation of this reflex wave.

The supplementary conditions necessary for the solution of system (47) can be obtained from a thorough consideration of the conditions for the motion of the reflex wave from the lowering of the water level and of the corresponding direct wave (see

[R33], p. 121). We will not derive these conditions here, but state them right away.

1. At time $t = 1076$ the reflex wave originates with the initial height $H = 2.2$ at $s = 0$.

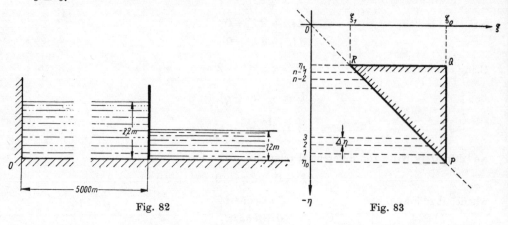

Fig. 82   Fig. 83

2. The front of the wave is propagated along the corresponding characteristic of the first family $\xi = $ const. according to the law

$$t = 1944\,H^{-\frac{3}{4}},$$

$$s = -\left(3\,\sqrt{gH} - 2\,\sqrt{2,2\,g}\right)t + 5000$$

3. For $s = 0$, U constant $= 0$.

We want to find the solution of this problem up to the instant when the front of the reflex wave hits the direct wave, which has a height $H_0 = 1.66$ m. This occurs at the time

$$T = 1944 \cdot 1{,}66^{-\frac{3}{4}} = 1330 \text{ sec}$$

Considering the $\xi\eta$-plane (Fig. 83), it is easy to see that in this plane the domain in which we should find the solution is represented by triangle PQR. In fact we have the condition for propagation of the wave front on the line $\xi = $ const., i.e. on the straight line PQ. Moreover, we have $s = 0$ for $U = 0$. Now

$$U = \frac{1}{2}\,(\xi + \eta).$$

This means $s = 0$ on the line $\xi + \eta = 0$, i.e. on the straight line PR. The values $\xi = \xi_0$ and $\eta = \eta_0 = -\xi_0$, which can be easily found, correspond to point P. For point Q we have

$$\xi = \xi_0,$$

$$\eta = \eta_1 = -\xi_0 + nh.$$

In order to find these figures, we note that at point P the initial head

$$H_0 = 2{,}2 \text{ m}$$

is given. Since $\qquad\qquad \lambda = 2\,\sqrt{gH}$

we have $$\lambda_0 = 2\sqrt{2,2g} = 2\sqrt{21,58} = 2 \cdot 4,645 = \underline{9,29}\,.$$

Likewise at Q the head $H_1 = 1.66$ is given. This gives

$$\lambda_1 = 2\sqrt{1,66g} = 2\sqrt{16,28} = 2 \cdot 4,035 = \underline{8,07}\,.$$

Then for the determination of ξ_0 and ξ_1 we have the equations

$$\lambda_0 = \frac{1}{2}\,(\xi_0 - \eta_0) = \frac{1}{2}\,(-2\eta_0) = -\eta_0\,,$$

$$\lambda_1 = \frac{1}{2}\,(\xi_1 - \eta_1) = \frac{1}{2}\,(\xi_0 - \eta_1),$$

whence it follows $$\xi_0 = -\eta_0 = 9,29\,,$$

$$\eta_1 = -2\lambda_1 + \xi_0 = -16,14 + 9,29 = -6,85$$

For the calculation of the required functional values, we divide the interval $(-\eta_0, -\eta_1)$ into 20 parts, putting $n = 20$ and

$$h = \frac{|\eta_1 - \eta_0|}{20} = 0,122$$

and plot the points P_{ik} with the coordinates

$$\xi = \xi_0 - ih$$

$$\eta = \eta_0 + kh = \xi_0 + kh.$$

At these points we will determine the values of the functions U, H, t, s. For this purpose we construct a table as shown in Fig. 84.

The horizontal rows of this table correspond to the lines

$$\xi = \text{const}$$

on the $\xi\eta$-plane, the vertical rows (columns) to the lines

$$\eta = \text{const.}$$

The points P, Q, R are indicated. The rows and columns are numbered from 0 to n inclusive; row i and column k meet in the square corresponding to point P_{ik} in the $\xi\eta$-plane. In each square of Fig. 84 we shall write four numbers as shown in Fig. 85. First of all the zero (top horizontal) line is filled in according to the formulas

$$U_{0k} = \frac{1}{2}\,(\xi_{0k} + \eta_{0k}) = \frac{1}{2}\,(\xi_{0k} - \xi_{0k} + kh) = k\,\frac{h}{2} = \underline{0,061k}\,, \quad H_{0k} = \frac{\lambda_{0k}^2}{4g}\,,$$

$$\lambda_{0k} = \frac{1}{2}\,(\xi_{0k} - \eta_{0k}) = \frac{1}{2}\,(\xi_0 + \xi_0 - kh) = \xi_0 - k\,\frac{h}{2}\,\underline{9,29 - 0,061k},$$

$$t_{0k} = 1944\,H_{0k}\,,$$

$$S_{0k} = -(3\sqrt{gH_{0k}} - 2\sqrt{2,2g})\,t_{0k} + 5000\,.$$

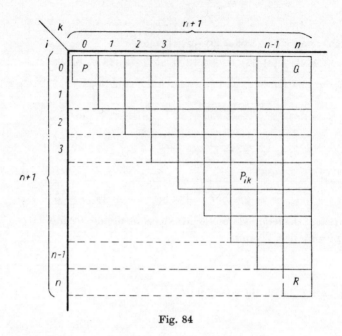

Fig. 84

U = m./sec.

H = m.

t = min.

s = m.

Fig. 85

Thus we get, for instance, with $K = 1$

$$U = 0{,}06,$$

$$\lambda = 9{,}23,$$

$$H = 2{,}17,$$

$$t = 18/07 = 18 \text{ min } 07 \text{ sec},$$

$$s = 50.$$

These values (except λ) are written into square (01) of Fig. 86. The remaining squares are filled in similarly.

Next comes computation of the values of the required quantities in the succeeding lines. For this purpose the equations (47) are used. The values ξ and η are known from before (they are computed for the lattice points of the $\xi\eta$-plane); this also implies that the values

$$U = \frac{1}{2}\,(\xi + \eta),$$

$$\lambda = \frac{1}{2}\,(\xi - \eta),$$

$$H = \frac{1}{4g}\,\lambda^2$$

are known. It remains to work out t and s.

i \ k	0	1	2	3	4	5	6
0	0,00 2,20 17|56 0	0,06 2,17 18|07 50	0,12 2,14 18|18 101	0,18 2,11 18|29 153	0,24 2,09 18|40 207	0,31 2,06 18|51 262	0,37 2,03 19|03 318
1		0,00 2,14 18|18 0	0,06 2,11 18|29 51	0,12 2,09 18|40 104	0,18 2,06 18|51 157	0,24 2,03 19|03 212	0,31 2,00 19|15 269
2			0,00 2,09 18|40 0	0,06 2,06 18|52 52	0,12 2,03 19|03 106	0,18 2,00 19|15 161	0,24 1,97 19|27 218
3				0,00 2,03 19|03 0	0,06 2,00 19|15 54	0,12 1,97 19|27 109	0,18 1,95 19|40 165
4					0,00 1,97 19|27 0	0,06 1,95 19|40 55	0,12 1,92 19|53 112
5		U — m/sec H — m t — min u. sec s — m				0,00 1,92 19|53 0	0,06 1,89 20|05 56
6							0,00 1,87 20|19 0

Fig. 86

i \ k	7	8	9	10	11	12	13
0	0,43 2,00 19|15 375	0,49 1,97 19|27 434	0,55 1,95 19|39 494	0,61 1,92 19|52 556	0,67 1,89 20|04 619	0,73 1,87 20|17 684	0,80 1,84 20|31 750
1	0,37 1,97 19|27 326	0,43 1,95 19|39 385	0,49 1,92 19|52 464	0,55 1,89 20|05 507	0,61 1,87 20|18 570	0,67 1,84 20|31 635	0,73 1,81 20|44 702
2	0,31 1,95 19|40 275	0,37 1,92 19|52 334	0,43 1,89 20|05 395	0,49 1,87 20|18 457	0,55 1,84 20|31 520	0,61 1,81 20|45 586	0,67 1,79 20|58 652
3	0,24 1,92 19|52 223	0,31 1,89 20|05 282	0,37 1,87 20|18 343	0,43 1,84 20|32 405	0,49 1,81 20|45 469	0,55 1,79 20|59 534	0,61 1,76 21|13 601
4	0,18 1,89 20|05 169	0,24 1,87 20|19 229	0,31 1,84 20|32 289	0,37 1,81 20|45 352	0,43 1,79 20|59 416	0,49 1,76 21|13 481	0,55 1,74 21|28 548
5	0,12 1,87 20|19 114	0,18 1,84 20|32 174	0,24 1,81 20|46 234	0,31 1,79 21|00 297	0,37 1,76 21|14 361	0,43 1,74 21|28 426	0,49 1,71 21|43 494
6	0,06 1,84 20|32 58	0,12 1,81 20|46 117	0,18 1,79 21|00 178	0,24 1,76 21|14 241	0,31 1,74 21|28 305	0,37 1,71 21|43 370	0,43 1,68 21|58 438

Fig. 86 (Continued)

k / i	14	15	16	17	18	19	20
0	0,86 1,81 20|44 818	0,92 1,79 20|58 887	0,98 1,76 21|12 938	1,04 1,74 21|26 1031	1,10 1,71 21|40 1106	1,16 1,68 21|55 11|83	1,22 1,66 22|10 1261
1	0,80 1,79 20|58 770	0,86 1,76 21|12 840	0,92 1,74 21|26 912	0,98 1,71 21|41 985	1,04 1,68 21|55 1060	1,10 1,66 22|10 1138	1,16 1,63 22|26 1217
2	0,73 1,76 21|12 721	0,80 1,74 21|27 791	0,86 1,71 21|41 863	0,92 1,68 22|56 936	0,98 1,66 22|11 1012	1,04 1,63 22|26 1090	1,10 1,61 22|43 1169
3	0,67 1,74 21|27 670	0,73 1,71 21|42 740	0,80 1,68 21|57 812	0,86 1,66 22|12 886	0,92 1,63 22|27 962	0,98 1,61 22|43 1040	1,04 1,58 22|59 1120
4	0,61 1,71 21|42 617	0,67 1,68 21|57 688	0,73 1,66 22|12 760	0,80 1,63 22|28 834	0,86 1,61 22|44 911	0,92 1,58 23|00 989	0,98 1,56 23|16 1069
5	0,55 1,68 21|58 563	0,61 1,66 22|13 634	0,67 1,63 22|29 707	0,73 1,61 22|44 781	0,80 1,58 23|01 858	0,86 1,56 23|17 936	0,92 1,54 23|34 1017
6	0,49 1,66 22|14 507	0,55 1,63 22|29 578	0,61 1,61 22|45 651	0,67 1,58 23|01 726	0,73 1,56 23|18 803	0,80 1,54 23|35 882	0,86 1,51 23|52 963

Fig. 86 (Continued)

i \ k	7	8	9	10	11	12	13
7	0,00 1,81 20|46 0	0,06 1,79 21|00 59	0,12 1,76 21|14 120	0,18 1,74 21|29 183	0,24 1,71 21|43 247	0,31 1,68 21|58 313	0,37 1,66 22|15 381
8		0,00 1,76 21|15 0	0,06 1,74 21|29 61	0,12 1,71 21|43 125	0,18 1,68 21|59 187	0,24 1,66 22|15 254	0,31 1,63 22|30 322
9			0,00 1,71 21|44 0	0,06 1,68 21|59 63	0,12 1,66 22|15 127	0,18 1,63 22|30 193	0,24 1,61 22|46 261
10				0,00 1,65 22|15 0	0,06 1,63 22|30 64	0,12 1,61 22|47 130	0,18 1,58 23|02 198
11					0,00 1,61 22|47 0	0,06 1,58 23|02 66	0,12 1,56 23|20 134
12						0,00 1,56 23|20 0	0,06 1,54 23|37 68
13							0,00 1,51 23|54 0

Fig. 86 (Continued)

i \ k	14	15	16	17	18	19˙	20
7	0,43 1,63 22|29 450	0,49 1,61 22|45 521	0,55 1,58 23|02 595	0,61 1,56 23|18 670	0,67 1,54 23|35 747	0,73 1,51 23|53 826	0,80 1,49 24|10 908
8	0,37 1,61 22|46 391	0,43 1,58 23|02 463	0,49 1,56 23|19 536	0,55 1,54 23|36 611	0,61 1,51 23|53 689	0,67 1,49 24|10 767	0,73 1,46 24|29 850
9	0,31 1,58 23|02 330	0,37 1,56 23|19 402	0,43 1,54 23|36 476	0,49 1,51 23|54 551	0,55 1,49 24|12 629	0,61 1,46 24|31 709	0,67 1,44 24|48 791
10	0,24 1,56 23|19 268	0,31 1,54 23|38 340	0,37 1,51 23|54 414	0,43 1,49 24|12 490	0,49 1,46 24|31 568	0,55 1,44 24|48 648	0,61 1,42 25|08 730
11	0,18 1,54 23|37 204	0,24 1,51 23|54 276	0,31 1,49 24|12 350	0,37 1,46 24|32 426	0,43 1,44 24|49 504	0,49 1,42 25|08 584	0,55 1,39 25|28 667
12	0,12 1,51 23|54 138	0,18 1,49 24|12 210	0,24 1,46 24|32 284	0,31 1,44 24|50 360	0,37 1,42 25|09 439	0,43 1,39 25|28 519	0,49 1,37 25|48 602
13	0,06 1,49 24|13 70	0,12 1,46 24|32 142	0,18 1,44 24|50 216	0,24 1,42 25|09 292	0,31 1,39 25|29 371	0,37 1,37 25|49 452	0,43 1,35 26|09 535

Fig. 86 (Continued)

i \ k	14	15	16	17	18	19	20
14	0,00 1,46 24|32 0	0,06 1,44 24|50 72	0,12 1,42 25|09 146	0,18 1,39 25|29 223	0,24 1,37 25|49 301	0,31 1,35 26|10 382	0,37 1,33 26|31 466
15		0,00 1,42 25|09 0	0,06 1,39 25|29 74	0,12 1,37 25|49 151	0,18 1,35 26|10 230	0,24 1,33 26|31 311	0,31 1,30 26|52 394
16			0,00 1,37 25|49 0	0,06 1,35 26|10 76	0,12 1,33 26|31 155	0,18 1,30 26|53 237	0,24 1,28 27|15 320
17				0,00 1,33 26|31 0	0,06 1,30 26|53 79	0,12 1,28 27|15 160	0,18 1,26 27|38 244
18					0,00 1,28 27|15 0	0,06 1,26 27|38 81	0,12 1,24 28|01 165
19						0,00 1,24 28|01 0	0,06 1,22 28|25 84
20							0,00 1,19 28|50 0

Fig. 86 (End)

From equations (47) we have

$$s_M - s_1 = \dot{W}_1(t_M - t_1), \\ s_M - s_2 = \Omega_2(t_M - t_2).$$ \quad (48)

In these equations W_1 denotes the magnitude of the coefficients in the first equation (47) at point 1:

$$W_1 = U_1 + \sqrt{gH_1}.$$

Similarly
$$\Omega_2 = U_2 - \sqrt{gH_2}.$$

The values s_M and t_M, in accordance with general principles, relate to point M, the intersection of the straight line running from points 1 and 2 in line with the chàracteristics; in our present case these directions coincide with those of the axes (Fig. 87). In the table of Fig. 86, the points 1, 2, and M shown in Fig. 88 correspond to the points 1, 2, M of Fig. 87. The calculation also follows this arrangement.

As coefficients W and Ω can be computed beforehand, one or even both of them can be taken immediately at point M instead of at point 1 (this can not be done generally, as the values of the coefficients depend on the coordinates of point M). In the numerical example in Fig. 86, coefficient Ω is taken at point M itself. To increase accuracy it is advantageous to take the semi-sum from the values at point 1 and at point M.

Particular care must be taken when determining t in the boxes on the diagonal (for $i = k$). In these squares $s = 0$, and therefore **one equation** is quite enough for finding t. Normally the equation of the **second family** (for $\eta = $ const.) will be taken, as, for the diagonal boxes, there are no adjacent horizontal squares in which all the necessary values could have been previously ascertained (Fig. 89). Thus we here complete the calculation in accordance with the formulas

$$t_M = t_2 - \frac{s_2}{\Omega_2} \quad (49)$$

or
$$t_M = t_2 - \frac{s_2}{\Omega_M} \quad (50)$$

Formula (50) is used in the numerical example in Fig. 86.

Example 2 ([R44], p. 122). Determination of the two-dimensional plastic deformation state around an elliptic orifice subject to a constant internal pressure p.

The problem is reduced to the solution of the system of equations

$$\text{I} \begin{cases} dy = \text{tg}\left(\varphi + \dfrac{\pi}{4}\right) dx, \\ \xi = \text{const}, \end{cases}$$

$$\text{II} \begin{cases} dy = \text{tg}\left(\varphi - \dfrac{\pi}{4}\right) dx, \\ \eta = \text{const} \end{cases}$$

where
$$\varphi = \frac{1}{2}(\xi - \eta), \\ \omega = \frac{1}{2}(\xi + \eta)$$

In these formulas x and y are the coordinates in the plane of the orifice, φ and ω are functions by means of which the stresses can be expressed according to the formulas

$$\sigma_x = k(-p + 2\omega + \cos 2\varphi),$$
$$\sigma_y = k(-p + 2\omega - \cos 2\varphi)$$

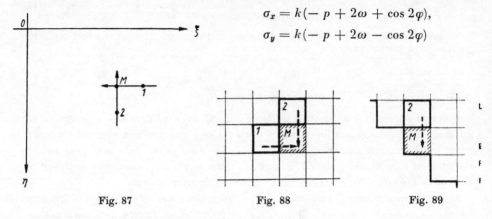

Fig. 87   Fig. 88   Fig. 89

The constant k is connected with the yield point σ_s by the equation

$$k = \frac{\sigma_s}{\sqrt{3}} \qquad \text{(Huber-Mises Hypothesis)}$$

The boundary conditions are as follows: On the boundary of the ellipse

$$x^2 + \frac{y^2}{(0,4)^2} = 1$$

the normal stress is given by the formula

$$\sigma_n = -kp. \tag{51}$$

Writing the equation of the ellipse

$$\frac{x^2}{a} + \frac{y^2}{b^2} = 1$$

in the parametric form

$$x = \frac{a^2 \sin \alpha}{\sqrt{a^2 \sin^2 \alpha + b^2 \cos^2 \alpha}}, \qquad y = -\frac{b^2 \cos \alpha}{\sqrt{a^2 \sin^2 \alpha + b^2 \cos^2 \alpha}}, \tag{52}$$

the boundary condition (51), written for the functions φ and ω, yields:

$$\omega = \frac{1}{2}, \qquad \varphi = \alpha \tag{53}$$

on ellipse (52) independently of the magnitude p.

Because of symmetry it is sufficient to find the solution in the quadrant $x \geqq 0$, $y \leqq 0$, corresponding to the values of the parameter α from 0 to $\frac{\pi}{2}$. We, therefore, seek the solution in the domain $-yPQx$, shown in Fig. 90. This domain is split into three subdomains:

I. $-yPS$ bounded by the negative y-axis and the characteristic PS running through point P;

II. $SPQR$ bounded by the arc of the ellipse and two characteristics of different families running through points P and Q;

III. RQx bounded by the x-axis and the characteristic RQ.

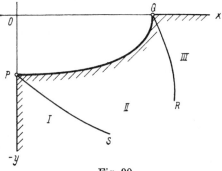

Fig. 90

It is, therefore, now a question of solving three mixed problems. The solution is set forth in Fig. 91.

The square in row i and column k of the traverse shown in this figure is denoted by $(i; k)$. The horizontal rows correspond to the lines $\eta = $ const. of the $\xi\eta$-plane, the columns to the lines $\xi = $ const. The squares $(0;10)$, $(1;9)$, . . . $(10;0)$ correspond to the boundary of the ellipse between the points P and Q. In these squares, the given values $\omega = 0.50$ and $\varphi = \alpha$ are recorded. The values of the parameter α are so adjusted that the corresponding points on the arc of the ellipse lie at approximately equal distances from each other. These values run:

$$\alpha = 0,000; \ 0,050; \ 0,098; \ . . .; \frac{\pi}{2} = 1,571.$$

The values x and y in these squares are worked out by formula (52) for the assigned values α.

The squares $(10;0)$, $(11;1)$, $(12;1)$, . . . correspond to the points on the x-axis. In them

$$\varphi = \frac{\pi}{2} = 1,571;$$

$$y = 0.$$

The values ω are calculated, starting from the fact that

$$\omega = \frac{1}{2}(\xi + \eta),$$

$$\varphi = \frac{1}{2}(\xi - \eta)$$

and the values η in the horizontal rows are constant. Since in squares $(0;10)$, $(1;9)$, . . . , $(10;0)$

$$\omega = \frac{1}{2}, \quad \varphi = \alpha$$

then

$$\xi = \frac{1}{2} + \alpha,$$

$$\eta = \frac{1}{2} - \alpha,$$

(55)

in these squares and in the squares (10;0), (11;1), . . . , on putting $\varphi = \dfrac{\pi}{2}$ and

$\eta = \dfrac{1}{2} - \alpha$ in the formula $\omega - \psi = \eta$, we find the following values for ω:

$$\omega = \frac{\pi}{2} + \frac{1}{2} - \alpha = 2{,}071 - \alpha :$$

If we take the values α from a field in the same horizontal row, we get

$$\omega_{11;1} = 2{,}071 - 0{,}961 = \underline{1{,}11,}$$

$$\omega_{12;2} = 2{,}071 - 0{,}650 = \underline{1{,}42,}$$

etc. These values ω are also noted in the corresponding squares. The values x are determined by the formulas

$$x_{ik} = x_{i-1,\,k} - y_{i-1,\,k} \operatorname{ctg}\left(\varphi_{i-1,\,k} - \frac{\pi}{4}\right)$$

In order to execute the calculation by these formulas, we must know the values x, y, φ, ω at the points on the left of the diagonal boxes (10;0), (11;1), . . . These values are obtained by completing the traverse squares corresponding to the interior points of domain II in Fig. 90 in accordance with the formulas

$$x_{ik} = \frac{y_{i-1,\,k} - y_{i,\,k-1} + x_{i,\,k-1} \operatorname{tg}\left(\varphi_{i,\,k-1} + \dfrac{\pi}{4}\right) - x_{i-1,\,k} \operatorname{tg}\left(\varphi_{i-1,\,k} - \dfrac{\pi}{4}\right)}{\operatorname{tg}\left(\varphi_{i,\,k-1} + \dfrac{\pi}{4}\right) - \operatorname{tg}\left(\varphi_{i-1,\,k} - \dfrac{\pi}{4}\right)},$$

$$y_{ik} = y_{i-1,\,k} + (x_{ik} - x_{i-1,\,k}) \operatorname{tg}\left(\varphi_{i-1,\,k} - \frac{\pi}{4}\right)$$

The values φ_{ik} and ω_{ik} can be calculated beforehand by formulas (54). Thus the traverse squares corresponding to domains II and III of Fig. 92 are filled in. In order to complete the remaining squares the boundary values at points (0;10), (1;11), (2;12), . . . corresponding to the y-axis (Fig. 92) must be postulated.

Clearly at these points

$$x = 0, \qquad \varphi = 0.$$

The values ω are found from the equations

$$2\omega = \xi + \eta,$$

$$2\varphi = \xi - \eta$$

for $\varphi = 0$. This gives $\qquad \omega = \xi.$

i \ k	0	1	2	3	4	5	6
0							
1							
2							
3							
4							0,50 0,358 0,69 0,29
5						0,50 0,273 0,58 0,33	0,54 0,315 0,65 0,37
6					0,50 0,205 0,46 0,36	0,53 0,238 0,54 0,40	0,58 0,282 0,61 0,45

Fig. 91

k \ i	7	8	9	10	11	12	13	14
0				0,50 1,571 1,00 0,00				
1			0,50 0,961 0,96 0,11	0,80 1,268 1,04 0,08	1,11 1,571 1,15 0,00			
2		0,50 6,050 0,89 0,19	0,64 0,808 0,97 0,19	0,96 1,110 1,09 0,17	1,26 1,413 1,23 0,10	1,42 1,571 1,34 0,00		
3	0,50 0,423 0,79 0,25	0,59 0,561 0,87 0,26	0,75 0,719 0,97 0,28	1,05 1,022 1,12 0,27	1,35 1,325 1,30 0,19	1,51 1,482 1,43 0,10	1,60 1,571 1,54 0,00	
4	0,56 0,415 0,76 0,32	0,65 0,504 0,85 0,35	0,80 0,642 0,96 0,37	1,11 0,964 1,14 0,37	1,41 1,267 1,35 0,29	1,57 1,425 1,51 0,19	1,66 1,513 1,63 0,10	1,71 1,571 1,75 0,00
5	0,60 0,373 0,73 0,41	0,69 0,461 0,82 0,45	0,85 0,619 0,94 0,48	0,15 0,923 1,16 0,48	1,45 1,225 1,41 0,41	1,61 1,382 1,59 0,30	1,70 1,471 1,71 0,21	
6	0,63 0,339 0,69 0,49	0,72 0,421 0,79 0,53	0,88 0,581 0,93 0,57	0,18 0,888 1,17 0,58				

Fig. 91 (Continuation)

k \ i	0	1	2	3	4	5	6
7				0,50 0,148 0,35 0,36	0,53 0,177 0,42 0,43	0,56 0,210 0,49 0,47	0,60 0,253 0,57 0,52
8			0,50 0,098 0,24 0,39	0,53 0,123 0,30 0,44	0,55 0,151 0,27 0,50	0,59 0,185 0,44 0,55	0,63 0,228 0,52 0,60
9		0,50 0,050 0,12 0,40	0,52 0,074 0,19 0,46	0,55 0,099 0,25 0,51	0,58 0,127 0,32 0,57	0,61 0,161 0,39 0,62	0,65 0,204 0,47 0,67
10	0,50 0,000 0,00 0,40	0,52 0,025 0,06 0,46	0,55 0,049 0,13 0,52	0,57 0,074 0,19 0,58	0,60 0,103 0,26 0,64	0,64 0,136 0,34 0,69	0,68 0,179 0,42 0,75
11		0,55 0,000 0,00 0,53	0,57 0,024 0,06 0,59	0,60 0,055 0,12 0,65			
12			0,60 0,000 0,00 0,66				

Fig. 91 (Continuation)

k i	7	8	9	10	11	12	13	14
7	0,66 0,311 0,65 0,57	0,75 0,399 0,75 0,61	0,91 0,557 0,90 0,66					
8	0,69 0,285 0,60 0,65	0,78 0,374 0,72 0,70						
9	0,71 0,261 0,56 0,73							
10								
11								
12								

Fig. 91 (End)

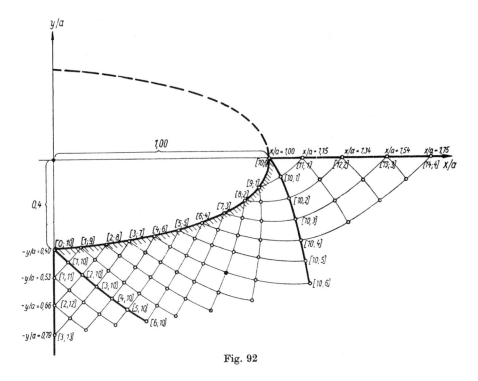

Fig. 92

As ξ is constant in the columns and is given by Formula (55) in the diagonal boxes (0;10), (1;9), . . . , we thus have

$$\omega_{11;1} = 0{,}50 + 0{,}05 = \underline{0{,}55},$$
$$\omega_{12;2} = 0{,}50 + 0{,}098 = \underline{0{,}60},$$

etc. The values y are found by the formulas

$$y_{ik} = y_{i,\,k-1} - x_{i,\,k-1}\,\mathrm{tg}\left(\varphi_{i,\,k-1} + \frac{\pi}{4}\right).$$

LIST OF EXAMPLES

LAPLACE and POISSON Equations

Page

Solution of Dirichlet Problem for a Square; Use of Lyusternik Corrections 42
Evaluation of Error by Means of Runge's Principle in the Solution of Dirichlet's
Problem for a Square 42
Torsion Problem for an H-girder; Use of Orr's Correction 42
Torsion Problem for a Keywayed Shaft; Solution with Refinement of the Network 53
Dirichlet Problem for an Ellipse; Solution with Mikeladze Improvement of
Boundary Values... 54
Solution of Neumann Problem for a Square 60
Solution of Third Boundary Value Problem for a Rectangle 62
Heat Conduction at the Corner of a Brick Wall.............................. 64
Torsion Problem for End of Aircraft Engine Shaft 73

Biharmonic Equation

Solution of the Biharmonic Equation for a Square, if the Value of the Required
Function and the Derivative of Its Normals on the Boundary Are Given 79
Determination of Deflection of a Uniformly Loaded Square Plate Resting Freely
on Its Edges... 79

Heat Conduction Equation

Determination of Temperature Condition of a Square if Temperature on Boundary
Is Given 89
Determination of Cooling of a Rod, when Temperature Kept Constant at 0°C. at
Its Extremities.. 93
Determination of Temperature Condition of an Ellipse when Temperature at
Boundary Is Given; Solution with Mikeladze Refinement of Boundary Values 94

Wave Equation

Oscillation of String with Given Starting Amplitude and Initial Velocity Zero 101

Hyperbolic Systems

Computation of Reflex Wave in a Channel, Disregarding Friction.............. 107
Computation of Stress Distribution in Plastic Zones Around an Elliptic Orifice 119

SELECTED BIBLIOGRAPHY

The following references are intended to assist the reader who requires additional background material. Works specifically referred to in the text are indicated by *. E, R, G, F, indicate that relevant text is written in English, Russian, German, or French respectively.

I — Works in English

E   1. BENNETT, A. A., MILNE, W. E., and BATEMAN, H., *Numerical Integration of Differential Equations*, National Research Council of the National Academy of Sciences, Washington D.C., 1933.

E   2. *DOUGLAS, J., "A Method of Numerical Solution of the Problem of Plateau," *Annals of Mathematics*, 29 (1929), 180–188.

E   3. EMMONS, H. W., "The Numerical Solution of Partial Differential Equations," *Quarterly Journal of Applied Mathematics* II, 3 (1944) 173–195.

E   4. FORD, L. R., *Differential Equations*, McGraw-Hill, New York, 1933.

E   5. FORSYTHE, G. E., *Numerical Analysis and Partial Differential Equations*. Wiley, New York, 1958.

E   6. FORSYTHE, G. E., *Finite Difference Methods for Partial Differential Equations*, Wiley, New York, 1960.

E   7. HARTREE, D. R., *Numerical Analysis*, London, Oxford University Press, 1952.

E   8. HILDEBRAND, F. B., *Introduction to Numerical Analysis*, McGraw-Hill, New York, 1956.

E   9. HOUSEHOLDER, A. S., *Principles of Numerical Analysis*, McGraw-Hill, New York, 1953.

E 10. KEMENY, J. G., SNELL, J. L., and THOMPSON, G. L., *Introduction to Finite Mathematics*, Prentice-Hall, New York, 1957.

E 11. KOPAL, Z., *Numerical Analysis*, Wiley, New York, 1955.

E 12. LADERMAN, J., and ABRAMOWITZ, M., "Application of Machines to Differencing of Tables," *Journal of the American Statistical Association*, 41 (1946), 233–237.

E 13. LANGER, R. E., *On Numerical Approximation*, University of Wisconsin Press, Madison (Wis.), 1959.

E 14. LEVY, H., and BAGGOTT, E. A., *Numerical Studies in Differential Equations*, Watts, London, 1934.

E 15. MILNE, W. E., "Numerical Integration of Ordinary Differential Equations," *American Mathematical Monthly*, 33 (1926), 455–460.

E 16. MILNE, W. E., *Numerical Calculus*, Princeton University Press, Princeton, (N. J.), 1949.

E 17. *ORR, J., "Several Cases of Non-circular Torsion Solved by Analysis and Direct Test," *Reports and Memoranda of the Royal Aeronautical Research Committee*, 1393 (1930).

E 18. *RICHARDSON, L. F., "The Approximate Arithmetical Solution by Finite Differences of Physical Problems Involving Differential Equations with an Application to the Stresses in a Masonry Dam," *Philosophical Transactions of the Royal Society of London*, A, 210 (1911), 307–357.

E 19. RICHTMEYER, R. D., *Difference Methods for Initial Value Problems*, Interscience, New York, 1957.

E 20. SALVADORI, M. G., and BARON, M. A., *Numerical Methods in Engineering*, Prentice-Hall, New York, 1952.

E 21. SCARBOROUGH, J. B., *Numerical Mathematical Analysis*, Johns Hopkins Press, Baltimore, 1955 (3rd. edn.).

E 22. STEFFENSEN, J. F., *Interpolation*, Williams and Wilkins, Baltimore, 1927.

E 23. *Tables of Lagrangian Interpolation Coefficients*, Columbia University Press, New York, 1944.

E 24. *THOM, A., "An Investigation of Fluid Flow in Two Dimensions," *Reports and Memoranda of the Royal Aeronautical Research Committee*, 1194 (1928).

E 25. ENGINEERING RESEARCH ASSOCIATES INC., *High-Speed Computing Devices*, McGraw-Hill, New York, 1950.

E 26. WHITTAKER, E. T., and ROBINSON, G., *The Calculus of Observations*, Blackie, Glasgow (Scotland), 1944 (4th edn.).

II — Works in Russian

R 27. *GAVRILOV, A. F., "Priblizhennoye chislennoye integrirovaniye telegrafnovo uravneniya," *Izvestiya Voenno-elektrotekhnicheskoy akademii RKKA*, 10 (1934), 3–17. [Approximate Numerical Integration of the Telegraph Equation].

R 28. *GAVRILOV, A. F., "Priblizhennoye chislennoye integrirovaniye telegrafnovo uravneniya, dlya sostavnoy linii," *Izvestiya Voenno-elektrotekhnicheskoy akademii RKKA*, 11 (1935), 115–127. [Approximate Numerical Integration of the Telegraph Equation for Inhomogeneous Lines].

R 29. *GERSHGORIN, S. A., "O priblizhennom integrirovanii uravnenii Laplasa i Puassona," *Izvestiya Leningradskovo politekhnicheskovo instituta*, 30 (1927). [On the Approximate Integration of the Laplace and Poisson Equations].

R 30. *GERSHGORIN, S. A., "Ob elektricheskikh setkakh dlya priblizhennovo resheniya differentsialnovo uravneniya Laplasa," *Zhurnal prikladnoy Fiziki*, 4 (1929), 3–29. [On Electrical Networks for the Approximate Solution of the Laplace Differential Equation].

R 31. *KANTOROVICH, L. V., and KRYLOV, V. I., *Metody priblizhennovo resheniya differentsialnykh uravneniy v chastnykh proizvodnykh*, ONTI, 1939. [Methods for the Approximate Solution of Partial Differential Equations].

R 32. *KHRISTIANOVICH, S. A., "O sverkhzvukovykh techeniyakh gaza," *Trudy TSAGI*, 543 (1941).
[On Hypersonic Gas Flows].

R 33. *KHRISTIANOVICH, S. A., *Neustanovivsheyesya dvizheniye v kanalakh i rekakh. Nekotorye voprosy mekhaniki sploshnoy sredy*, Izd. AN SSSR, 1938.
[Non-steady movements in waterways and rivers. Some questions on continuum mechanics].

R 34. *LYUSTERNIK, L. A., "Zamechaniya k chislennomu resheniyu krayevykh zadach uravneniya Laplasa i vychisleniyu sobstvennykh znacheniy metodom setok," *Trudy Matematicheskovo instituta im. V. A. Steklova*, 20 (1947), 49–64.
[Notes on the Numerical Solution of Boundary Value Problems of the Laplace Equation and for Computation of Eigenvalues by Means of the Method of Differences.]

R 35. *MIKELADZE, C. E., "O chislennom integrirovanii differentsialnykh uravneniy s chastnymi proizvodnymi," *Izvestiya Akademii Nauk SSSR po Otd. yestyestv. i matemat. nauk*, 6 (1934), 819.
[On the Numerical Integration of Partial Differential Equations].

R 36. *MIKELADZE, C. E., *Chislennye metody integrirovaniya differentsialnykh uravneniy v chastnykh proizvodnykh, dissertatsiya*, 1936.
[Thesis on Numerical Methods of Integration of Partial Differential Equations].

R 37. *MIKELADZE, C. E., "O chislennom integrirovanii uravneniy ellipticheskovo i parabolicheskovo tipa," *Izvestiya AN SSSR, seriya matematicheskaya*, 5 (1941), 57–73.
[Numerical Integration of Elliptic and Parabolic Type Equations].

R 38. *PANOV, D. Y., "O priblizhennom chislennoi reshenii $\varDelta u = a^2 \frac{\partial u}{\partial t}$,"
Matematicheskiy sbornik, 40 (1933), 373–393.
[On the Approximate Numerical Solution of the Equation $\varDelta u = a^2 \frac{\partial u}{\partial t}$].

R 39. *PANOV, D. Y., "Priblizhennoye graficheskoye resheniye krayevykh zadach uravneniya Laplasa," *Trudy TSAGI*, (1934).
[Approximate Graphical Solution of Boundary Value Problems for Laplace Type Partial Differential Equations].

R 40. *PANOV, D. Y., *Chislennoye resheniye krayevykh zadach differentsialnykh uravneniy v chastnykh proizvodnykh*, 1934.
[Numerical Solution of Boundary Value Problems in Partial Differential Equations] (Supplement to Russian Translation of Scarborough's *Numerical Mathematical Analysis*, 1st edn.). See E 21.

R 41. *PANOV, D. Y., "Chislennoye resheniye krayevykh zadach differentsialnykh uravneniy chastnykh proizvodnykh ellipticheskovo tipa," *Uspekhi* matematiches kikhnauk, 4 (1937), 23–33.
[Numerical Solution of Boundary Value Problems for Partial Differential Equations of the Elliptic Type].

R 42. *SOBOLEV, S. L., *Uravneniya matematicheskoy fiziki*, Gostekhizdat, 1947. [Mathematical Physical Equations].

R 43. *SOKOLOVSKIY, V. V., *Statika sypuchey sredy*, Izd. AN SSSR, 1942. [Statics of Noncohesive Media].

R 44. *Sokolovskiy, V. V., *Teoriya plastichnosti*, Izd. AN SSSR, 1945. [Plasticity Theory].

R 45. *Yushkov, P. P., "O primenenii treugolnykh setok dlya chislennovo resheniya uravneniya teploprovodnosti," *Prikladnaya matematika i mekhanika*, 12 (1948), 223–226.
[Use of Triangular Networks in Solving the Heat Conduction Equation].

III — Works in German

G 46. Biermann, O., *Vorlesungen über mathematische Näherungsmethoden*, Vieweg Brunswick, 1905.

G 47. *Collatz, L., "Bemerkungen zur Fehlerabschätzung für das Differenzenverfahren bei partiellen Differentialgleichungen," *Zeitschrift für angewandte Mathematik und Mechanik*, 13 (1933), 56–57.

G 48. *Courant, R., "Über Randwertaufgaben bei partiellen Differentialgleichungen," *Zeitschrift für angewandte Mathematik und Mechanik*, 6 (1926), 322–325.

G 49. *Courant, R., Friedrichs, K., Lewy, H., "Über die partiellen Differenzengleichungen der mathematischen Physik," *Mathematische Annalen*, 100 (1928), 32–74.

G 50. *Courant, R., and Hilbert, D., *Methoden der mathematischen Physik*, Springer, Berlin, 1937.

G 51. *Gershgorin, S. A., "Fehlerabschätzung für das Differenzverfahren zur Lösung partieller Differentialgleichungen," *Zeitschrift für angewandte Mathematik und Mechanik*, 10 (1930), 373–382.

G 52. *Hencky, H., "Die numerische Bearbeitung von partiellen Differentialgleichungen in der Technik," *Zeitschrift für angewandte Mathematik und Mechanik*, 2 (1922), 58–66.

G 53. *Liebmann, H., "Die angenäherte Ermittlung harmonischer Funktionen und konformer Abbildungen," *Sitzungsberichte der Bayrischen Akademie der Wissenschaften, Math.-Phys. Klasse*, 1918, 385–436.

G 54. *Lyusternik, L., "Über einige Anwendungen der direkten Methoden der Variationsrechnung," *Matematicheskiy Sbornik*, 23 (1926), 173–201.

G 55. *Marcus, H., *Die Theorie elastischer Gewebe und ihre Anwendung auf die Berechnung biegsamer Platten*, Springer, Berlin, 1932 (2nd edn.).

G 56. *Panov, D. Y., "Über die angenäherte numerische Lösung des Problems der Wärmeleitung," *Zeitschrift für angewandte Mathematik und Mechanik*, 12 (1932), 185–188.

G 57. *Runge, C., "Über eine Methode, die partielle Differentialgleichung $\Delta u = $ const numerisch zu integrieren," *Zeitschrift für Mathematik und Physik*, 56 (1908), 225–232.

G 58. Runge, C., and König, *Numerisches Rechnen*, Springer, Berlin, 1924.

G 59. Smirnov, V. I., *Aufgaben zu den partiellen Differentialgleichungen der mathematischen Physik*, Verlag der Wissenschaften, Berlin, 1955.

G 60. *Willers, F. A., *Methoden der praktischen Analysis*, de Gruyter, Berlin, 1928.

G 61. *WOLF, F., "Über die angenäherte numerische Berechnung harmonischer und biharmonischer Funktionen," *Zeitschrift für angewandte Mathematik und Mechanik*, 6 (1926), 118–150.

IV — Works in French

F 62. *MASSAU, J., *Mémoire sur l'intégration graphique des équations aux dérivées partielles*, Delporte, Ghent, 1903.

F 63. NÖRLUND, *Leçons sur les séries d'interpolation*, Borel, Paris, 1926.